Perspectives in Elementary School Mathematics

A *Publication in*

MERRILL'S MATHEMATICS EDUCATION SERIES

Under the editorship of

M. Vere DeVault
The University of Wisconsin

F. Joe Crosswhite
The Ohio State University

Perspectives in Elementary School Mathematics

M. Vere DeVault
The University of Wisconsin

Thomas E. Kriewall
The University of Wisconsin

Charles E. Merrill Publishing Company   Columbus, Ohio

A Bell & Howell Company

Library of Congress Catalog Card Number: 69-11961

1 2 3 4 5 6 7 8 9 10 11 12 13 14 15—76 75 74 73 72 71 70 69

Printed in the United States of America

Preface

Every classroom teacher of elementary school mathematics knows there is no shortage of advice from the experts regarding what ought to be taught and how to teach it. The performance record of the advice givers, however, has not always been up to expectations. Those teachers whose experience extends beyond the median 3 or 4 years of service have very likely recognized a number of cycles in which some cherished method or idea has been cast aside only to be returned again in esteem another day. Thus, it is natural, indeed good, that new ideas are questioned and tested until their value is known.

Unfortunately, some teachers have become hardened by this experience and have adopted the attitude: "What good thing can come out of theory, research, and academia?" They find it easy to recount to the neophyte teacher how some new suggestion is nothing but an old practice dressed in modern garb.

Nevertheless, for both experienced and novice teachers, it is important to the effectiveness of teaching to understand not only past failures, but what has been learned from past mistakes, what forces have initiated movements for reform, and why certain practices seem to cycle in and out of favor. Chapter 1 of this book is designed to fill this need. The history of mathematics education in the United States is traced in three important eras (Early National, Industrial Expansion, Modern), outlining the major problems, movements, mistakes, and successes of each. From this brief treatment, the reader should gain the perspective necessary to see the modern mathematics-reform in context, and therefore be better able to fit his own instruction to its purpose and spirit.

One of the unfortunate historical facts of mathematics education has been the almost complete failure in communication between the community of mathematicians and those educators who, from about 1920 to 1955, were responsible for the preparation of both instructional materials and elementary school teachers. Consequently, instructional practice in the grades has for years been largely independent of progress in and influence from the field of mathematics. For the most part, the traditional program never got beyond matters which were of interest to mathematicians back around the sixteenth century or earlier. Yet, the last 450 years, and especially the last 50, have been years of mathematical progress unparalleled in the history of man. Though it is difficult to render the spirit of this advance accurately to nonmathematicians, an effort is made in the conclusion of Chapter 1 to sketch this development in the hope that the reader will better sense what mathematicians are seeking to contribute to the modern mathematics movement.

Good teaching is not only very practical in style but necessarily grounded in some theoretical frame of reference. Two kinds of theory have been of historical importance in shaping the beliefs and practices which have guided classroom instruction in arithmetic. Theoretical psychology, in its growth from infancy a bare century ago, is one of these; the even newer curriculum theory is the other. In Chapter 2, the essential relationship between the philosophical and psychological view of man and instructional technique is reviewed.

With this background, Chapter 3 synthesizes the essential features of content, view of learner, role of teacher, and instructional method into a systems model of curriculum. This synthesis serves not so much as a predictive model or theory, but one which offers organizational guidelines in thinking about the "inputs" (content, learner, teacher, instruction) and the "output" (learning experiences) of educational endeavors. It also serves as a useful guideline to the subsequent discussion of the more practical aspects of elementary school mathematics instruction.

Chapters 4, 5, and 6 articulate the systems model in practical terms. Chapter 4 focuses primarily on the long-range decision making needed to build a systematic, well-organized curriculum. Since the textbook continues to serve as the principal embodiment of the curriculum, we also discuss textbook selection in this chapter.

Chapters 5 and 6 are both related to the short-term or instructional decision which constitutes the bulk of the teacher's daily task. Chapter

5 treats the methods and materials of instruction, while Chapter 6 is devoted to the means of evaluating both learning and instruction.

M. Vere DeVault
Thomas E. Kriewall

September, 1968 Madison, Wisconsin

Contents

ix

HISTORICAL BACKGROUND OF THE MODERN MATHEMATICS REFORM

No man putteth a piece of a new garment upon an old; if otherwise, then both the new maketh a rent, and the piece that was taken out of the new agreeth not with the old.

And no man putteth new wine into old skins; else the new wine will burst the skins, and be spilled, and the skins shall perish. But the new wine must be put into new skins; and both are preserved.

No man also having drunk old wine straightway desireth new: for he saith: The old is better.

Luke 5:36-9

THE HISTORY OF MATHEMATICS EDUCATION IN THE ELEMENTARY SCHOOL[1]

Our attention in this historical review is focused on, but not entirely restricted to, mathematics curriculum in the American elementary school. Of special interest is the relation between present classroom instruction and the reforms which have been advocated at various

---

[1]The material of this section has been gathered from a number of sources. For a comprehensive survey of modern education, see Frederick Eby, *The De-*

Illustration 1

The compact Colburn book compared to its present-day equivalent-content series.

times in the past. History reveals the fate of efforts at reform and thereby suggests the mixture of hope and caution with which we might temper our evaluation of the present evolutionary movement, known variously as "modern mathematics" or "the new math."

The modern mathematics movement did not, of course, just happen. To begin to see the purpose it has or to assess whatever value it possesses, one must examine it in the context of the issues which gave it

---

velopment of Modern Education (Englewood Cliffs, N.J.: Prentice-Hall, Inc., 1952). For an outstanding analysis of progressivism in American education, see Lawrence A. Cremins, *The Transformation of the School* (New York: Alfred A. Knopf, 1961). Further information on arithmetic in the elementary curriculum is available in Chester W. Harris (ed.), *Encyclopedia of Educational Research* (New York: The Macmillan Company, 1960), 3rd Edition.

birth. Many of the most crucial issues, as we shall see, have had less to do with the subject matter itself than with other broader concerns directed toward reform of all schooling. The effects on arithmetic, although incidental when viewed in the broad perspective of the development of education in America, nevertheless have been profound and for the most part ironic. The soaring vision of our country's great educational architects—for example, Horace Mann, William T. Harris, John Dewey—has been frequently distorted through translation. To the classroom teacher, their ideals became caricatures which too often produced only empty slogans and malpractice. Our hope is that we can learn and benefit from a review of history's lessons and, by so doing, accomplish our present efforts at improvement with maximum fidelity to the aspirations on which they are founded.

An examination of the background and context of modern mathematics reform in the elementary school certainly would be short-sighted if we chose to outline simply the history of *mathematics* and subsequently to advise some set of values and principles by which future practice ought to be guided. We begin rather by sketching the picture of development of the elementary schools, together with the forces which have brought them to their present position. We outline in each era how values have been chosen, attacked, and re-cast, and how in this broad panorama of change, arithmetic instruction has been affected.

Colonial and Early National Period (1700-1870)

The Beginning of Schooling

What were the early schools in America like? It is tempting to visualize little red schoolhouses with children sitting properly in neat rows of desks, attentively listening to a humorless and harsh teacher proceeding to impart the three R's through the deadly efficiency of hickory-stick methodology. Actually, the very first schools were the result of some foresight and considerable caution exercised by the respective governments which colonized the new land. The general practice was to imitate the organization and purpose of schools in the motherland, a practice designed to assure continuity of the culture as well as continued allegiance to God and king. Thus, Dutch and Puritan schools were theocratic and authoritarian. Ministers and schoolmasters typically accompanied the colonists and immediately set about building rough-hewn log churches and schools in each new settlement. In English territories, schools emerged in accordance with the old practice of endowment by wealthy individuals or the crown.

For the most part, early teachers were college graduates, ministers, schoolmasters, or experienced teachers of elementary schools attracted to the freedom, promise, or call of duty in the new land. Religious instruction was common to all schools. Beyond that, considerable differences in purpose and program could be found. Some schools emphasized writing, others reading; some prepared the young especially in the classics for college, others stressed fundamentals and apprenticeship designed to furnish youngsters with a marketable skill.

The Beginning of Arithmetic Instruction

Arithmetic's role, at first, was regarded as less important than that of religion, reading, and writing. But as commerce increased, the utilitarian value of ciphering became increasingly valued in the general training of the young. By the 1700's, on the basis of its practical merits, an equal place was secured for arithmetic in the elementary curriculum.

How was arithmetic taught? Instruction varied, of course, with respect to schools and teachers. In some areas, several schools shared one teacher who spent his time at each in proportion to the financial support he received. He might spend as little as a month or two every 3 years at a school and have perhaps only a single pupil in some locales. In other cases teachers, pupils, and textbooks were available in richer supply.

Some features of methodology were common, however, in teaching arithmetic. Children of approximately age 10 and up were expected to learn by rote and drill how to perform with speed and accuracy the fundamental operations necessary to commerce. Children typically were tutored individually, a single text and drill book serving as guide for pupils of all ages and abilities.

Early textbooks were mainly of English origin and consisted of such fare as fundamental operations on whole numbers and fractions, proportion, and mixture problems. Exercises were drawn for the most part from the world of commerce. Following the War of Independence, American authors set about preparing texts to reflect the educational as well as political independence of the New World. The first such arithmetic text was written by the Harvard mathematician Isaac Greenwood in 1729. But the first to gain wide use was an abridged version of the *New and Complete System of Arithmetic* by Nicholas Pike. True to the tenor of its time, the Pike text was, above all, practical. In addition to teaching the four fundamental operations on whole numbers, common fractions, and decimal fractions, many pages were devoted to rules for changing money from the colonies' system to that of the federal government and back again.

The American Schools' First Crisis

With the end of the Revolutionary War, a variety of serious problems beset the schools, some of which sound distinctly familiar to the modern ear. Teachers were in short supply and few provisions had been made for increasing their number. Schools were physically inadequate, suffering from a chronic deficiency of financial support. Finally, profound disagreement existed concerning what purpose and organization would best fit the schools to assist in building the new society. On the one hand were the advocates of centralized instruction and indoctrination of democratic principles; on the other were those who argued for local control and cultivation of the ability to think for oneself. More to the point, most children were not in school at all. In the face of endemic poverty and the hard life of a frontier society, the value of formal education was not obvious. Furthermore, many held that education was the prerogative of the church and the home and were not willing to send their children to public schools even where free instruction was available.

The quality of education, as a result of these many difficulties, suffered a perceptible decline in the period from about 1790 to 1830. Instruction reached its lowest point with the introduction of the Lancastrian system, around 1812, in which large groups of children were taught by a single teacher assisted by older children who served as monitors. Thus the stage was set for the first great reform of American schools, the difficult struggle to establish universal education.

For our purposes, it is sufficient to examine the visions which first won people to the support of public schools and ultimately to the acceptance of the idea of compulsory attendance. Both ideas, tax-supported schools and compulsory attendance as advocated by Horace Mann and others, were to have far-reaching effects on the importance and method of teaching arithmetic in the schools.

Crime, disease, and poverty then as now were everywhere apparent for the eye to see. Mann harnessed the power of public opinion to the support of universal education by picturing the schools as the balance wheel of social machinery, the agency which would improve man himself and thereby eliminate crime, improve health, and increase wealth. Such an argument capitalized on the prevailing sentiment that human life was capable of unlimited improvement. It forcefully linked the schools to the destiny of the young republic.

The gradual emergence and acceptance of the idea of compulsory and free public education brought about significant changes in classroom practice. Tax laws were passed to provide a financial stability which the schools had not known before. For the first time provisions were made to train elementary school teachers. Lancastrian practice rapidly subsided as more teachers became available. Enrollments grew, and the need for more efficient teaching techniques increased. But now a persistent question needed to be answered. How, in a system of education proclaimed to be the salvation of the new democratic order, could children at once be *freed* to become adults capable of intelligent independent action and at the same time be *guided* to achieve competency in their academic work? The answer was to blend the naturalism of Rousseau (1712-1778), the pedagogy of Pestalozzi (1746-1827), and the psychology of the phrenologists (faculty psychology) into an American hybrid of belief and practice. The value and place of arithmetic in the curriculum was determined by the tenets of faculty psychology; the methods by which it was to be imparted were Pestalozzian.

The New Foundations of Arithmetic Instruction

First of all, the adaptation from Europe of Pestalozzi's techniques, which stressed the use of physical objects in the development of arithmetic skills, must be understood and appreciated as a genuine breakthrough in methodology. The problem that he attacked and solved grew out of the fact that Western civilization was still struggling to adapt to the "new" system of Hindu-Arabic place-value notation. The old system, which consisted of performing calculations on an abacus and recording only the results in Roman notation, was far easier for the ordinary man to comprehend and master than the more abstract and powerful notation imported from the East which took over roles *both* as a computing *and* recording device. By using "object lessons," Pestalozzi employed the simplicity of concrete illustrations to clarify the meaning of the base-place value numeration scheme. The startling effect of his method was that the earliest age at which children could successfully be taught arithmetic computation was reduced from 10 to 5 years.

Faculty psychology was especially appealing to the advocates of universal education precisely because it suggested human behavior could be improved. The scheme was marvelously simple. The school

Illustration 2

A comparison of two methods of computation—the Hindu-Arabic numeration system combined both the computational functions of the abacus and the recording function of Roman numeration into one operational system.

would guide the child to exercise desirable mental faculties while forcibly suppressing the use of undesirable ones, thus producing a free adult capable of the intelligent and moral judgment necessary to the perfection of democratic society. The role of arithmetic was important to this process. Reason was one of the 37 faculties. What subject was better fitted for its exercise!

The new instructional practice was soon reflected in a new generation of textbooks. In 1821, Warren Colburn's book, *First Lessons in Arithmetic on the Plan of Pestalozzi,* was published and became in subsequent years the arithmetic text *par excellence* of the elementary schools. The book stressed the development of mental power through an understanding of the rationale of arithmetic, a practice as dramatic and challenging then as teaching the structure of mathematics is viewed in many quarters today. Colburn, like reformers today, was careful not to de-emphasize the utilitarian values of arithmetic. Three out of four of the first thousand exercises were for drill! However, the striking feature of the text lay in its attempt to introduce arithmetic inductively to children in the context of socially meaningful illustrations and materials. Postponement of drill was advocated until an understanding of the basic processes had been developed. Thus we

LONG DIVISION: INDUCTIVE EXPLANATION

Dividing by Large Numbers

1. Just before Christmas Frank's father sent 360 oranges to be divided among the children in Frank's class. There are 29 children. How many oranges should each child receive? How many oranges will be left over?

Here is the best way to find out:

12 *and 12 remainder* 29⟌360 29 ——— 70 58 —— 12	*Think how many 29s there are in 36. 1 is right.* *Write 1 over the 6 of 36. Multiply 29 by 1.* *Write the 29 under the 36. Subtract 29 from 36.* *Write the 0 of 360 after the 7.* *Think how many 29s there are in 70. 2 is right.* *Write 2 over the 0 of 360. Multiply 29 by 2.* *Write the 58 under 70. Subtract 58 from 70.* *There is 12 remainder.* *Each child gets 12 oranges, and there are 12 left over. This is right, for 12 multiplied by 29 = 348, and 348 + 12 = 360.*

*   *   *   *   *   *

8.

31⟌99,587

In No. 8, keep on dividing by 31 until you have used the 5, the 8, and the 7, and have four figures in the quotient.

9.	**10.**	**11.**	**12.**	**13.**
22⟌253	22⟌2895	21⟌8891	22⟌290	32⟌16,368

Check your results for 9, 10, 11, 12, and 13.

1. The boys and girls of the Welfare Club plan to earn money to buy a victrola. There are 23 boys and girls. They can get a good second-hand victrola for $5.75. How much must each earn if they divide the cost equally?

Here is the best way to find out:

.25 23⟌$5.75 46 ——— 115 115 ———	*Think how many 23s there are in 57. 2 is right.* *Write 2 over the 7 of 57. Multiply 23 by 2.* *Write 46 under 57 and subtract. Write the 5 of 575 after the 11.* *Think how many 23s there are in 115. 5 is right.* *Write 5 over the 5 of 575. Multiply 23 by 5.* *Write the 115 under the 115 that is there and subtract.* *There is no remainder.* *Put $ and the decimal point where they belong.* *Each child must earn 25 cents. This is right, for $.25 multiplied by 23 = $5.75.*

2. Divide $71.76 equally among 23 persons. How much is each person's share?

3. Check your result for No. 2 by multiplying the quotient by the divisor.

Find the quotients. Check each quotient by multiplying it by the divisor.

4.	**5.**	**6.**	**7.**	**8.**
23⟌$99.13	25⟌$18.50	21⟌$129.15	13⟌$29.25	32⟌$73.92

1 bushel = 32 qt.

9. How many bushels are there in 288 qt.?   **10.** In 192 qt.?
11. In 416 qt.?

Illustration 3

Layout of Colburn's text, showing how inductive methodology was incorporated into textbooks in the early 1800's.

see the harbinger of meaningful instruction, the discovery method, and concern for the appropriate use of drill—all matters which were to remain of central concern for more than another century. Importantly, Colburn's book made little change in the content of arithmetic, a deficiency common to this and successive texts which no arithmetic reform would seriously challenge until the 1950's.

Industrialization and Immigration (1870-1950)

Growing Pains of the Young Educational System

One by one, with Massachusetts leading the way, the states began building the American school system into a form similar to that which we see today. By the 1860's, a half-dozen states had initiated free secular systems and a few had passed compulsory attendance laws. In order to provide teachers for the schools, the normal school idea was imported from France—a subcollege-level school dedicated solely to the preparation of elementary school teachers. The first of these schools opened its doors in 1839. From such schools flowed once again the vital supply of trained teachers which had been interrupted by the Revolutionary War.

Following the Civil War, the educational system grew rapidly at every level, evolving by 1880 into an articulated sequence of the 8-year grade school, 4-year high school, and 4-year college or professional school. But as the schools struggled to consolidate their hard-won victories, new and formidable forces challenged cherished values. The stresses of immigration and industrialization now strained the schools to the limit. As pupil-teacher ratios rocketed past 60 to 1, the need for efficient administrative organization dominated most other considerations. As a result of the leadership of William Torrey Harris, earlier experiments in grouping children into grades by chronological age soon became a standard practice. Emphasis was placed on school record keeping, building maintenance and needs, adequate health and sanitary facilities, as well as grade keeping to measure student progress.

The curriculum also was shaped by the new forces, although a fundamental divergence of views arose. Those who saw the school, the institution, as the preserver of democratic society, that is, the only device by which the foreign-born would become Americanized, advocated and implemented the curriculum strongly reflecting the tenets of Idealism and Humanism. On the other hand, for those who saw the school as the means of supplying trained manpower to industry, such education seemed not only irrelevant to the important needs of life but also incapable of satisfying the nation's growing demand for skilled manpower. Led by such men as Calvin Woodward, this latter movement resulted in the beginning of the now extensive system of vocational and trade schools.

Arithmetic in the Discipline Era

It is hardly surprising that discipline-based methodology became a way of life in most schools by the late 1800's. Orderly behavior was put at a premium; mastery of the fundamentals (mathematics, geography, literature, grammar, and history) became the most valued intellectual goal of the elementary schools. Rote instruction and drill in fundamentals were the order of the day. Arithmetic may have been given a vital role in the new order (Harris called it one of the "five windows of the soul"), but stultifying methodology combined with harshness for those pupils guilty of faulty responses dealt a blow to the popularity of the subject from which it is struggling to recover yet today.

The grading of the schools also had its effect on arithmetic instruction. Certainly this practice produced many new concerns, such as grade-placement and readiness, but perhaps most fundamental was the change brought about in the nature of textbooks. Prior to this time, a single text typically sufficed for pupils at all instructional levels. But as the schools became graded, publishers quickly adapted to the new arrangement and produced graded arithmetic books. The first of these appeared in 1877, written by Joseph Ray. This series was oriented to faculty psychology and leaned heavily on the content of Colburn's earlier treatise. Its chief contribution was the attempt to simplify the presentation and incorporate the ideas into a graded scheme. Thus the arithmetic, though segmented, differed little in content from that of Pike's text of the century before.

The effect on instructional techniques was profound, however. Now each teacher was assigned a certain segment of arithmetic to teach. The children from the lowest grade to the highest had as their chief goal the mastery of skills and the memorization of facts. The teacher was controlled by a printed course of study, a set of textbooks, and the necessity of preparing his class to pass certain examinations on the content of a specific number of printed pages. As the nineteenth century came to a close, instruction in arithmetic had reached an extreme of empty formalism. In a vain effort to secure the elusive goals of speed and accuracy, more and more time was being devoted to arithmetic with little visible return on the investment. Obviously, this formalism could not last.

The Reaction to Formalism

It seems that no educational idea or practice ever disappears completely. Like quanta of matter-energy with a peculiar law of conservation all their own, old ideas and old practices continue to exist, combining endlessly with the radical ideas of reform, tempering them and sometimes eclipsing them to emerge once again as a dominant force in educational practice. Such was the tale of arithmetic instruction during the early years of the most momentous reform movement in American education, which came to be known as Progressivism.

By 1890, opposition and resentment against the increasingly formal, bookish, unrelated-to-life, harsh educational practice had reached the flash point. The spark which ignited the flames of protest is generally acknowledged to have been struck by the articles of Joseph Mayer Rice[2] published in *The Forum* during the winter of 1892-93. A pediatrician turned educational investigator, his stinging criticism missed few of the plentiful array of targets.

After an extensive trip around the country in which he documented his charges, Rice returned to write and publish his sensational articles. He painted a dismal picture of political corruption, public apathy, and incompetent instructors working to ruin the schools. On every hand, with a few notable exceptions, he found the same pattern: rote, drill, meaningless verbalization. The exceptions he noted and labeled as "progressive" were certain schools at Minneapolis; Indianapolis; La-Porte, Indiana; and Francis Parker's famous Cook County Normal School. This citation not only turned the spotlight on these schools but helped in establishing the canons of quality which would guide the reconstruction of the schools in the coming Progressive Era.

Rice called for action. First, he urged that control of the schools be removed from the corrupt hands of the politicians and turned over to "professional" educators. Second, he insisted that every effort be made to improve the competency of teachers.

The sensational criticism of the schools by the press was hardly a revelation to experience-toughened professionals like Charles Eliot, then president of Harvard. He had led efforts to effect improvements

---

[2]For a brief biography of Rice, see *The National Cyclopaedia of American Biography*, XII, 203-4.

for several years prior to the time of Rice's enlightenment. Nevertheless, the strident chorus of harsh criticism which arose after Rice's articles provided the needed impetus to get the reform moving. In 1893 and again in 1895, prestigious committees sponsored by the National Education Association (NEA), the first being chaired by Eliot, undertook respectively a thorough study of secondary and elementary practices. Although their recommendations were still very much rooted in formal discipline thinking, the effects reached the very roots of education. Among the prodigious consequences of their report, cited by Eby as "one of the most important educational documents ever issued in the United States," would be (1) secondary curricula shaped to a common mold by the need to conform to a "unit system" for college entrance; (2) the emergence of junior high schools in response to the urgent need to begin many studies earlier; (3) laboratory work encouraged, especially in the sciences; (4) the hour-credit system established in colleges; (5) elementary schools reorganized around K-6 rather than K-8; (6) elementary curricula, seriously fragmented, unified by the broad-fields concept of organization; and certainly not least, (7) innovation freed from the then common notion that experimentation with children especially at the taxpayer's expense was a dangerous, probably subversive, and certainly unethical practice.

The Impact of Early Psychologists

If the committees of the NEA were prime movers of administrative and curricular reform at the turn of the century, no less important was the work of several outstanding individuals in building the foundations which could support the new order. From the genius of men like William James, G. Stanley Hall, John Dewey, and Edward Thorndike flowed fresh concepts of mind, man, and society which would challenge the entrenched faculty-discipline viewpoint as well as the views of one another. Building on these bases, education entered one of its most active periods of innovation and reform.

William James: Learning by Doing. The philosopher William James, teacher of Hall and Thorndike, was an early advocate of the idea that we learn by doing. This emphasis, which also influenced Dewey's thinking, was the root source of the trend in the early 1900's toward instruction organized around problem-oriented activities and projects. But James also helped reinforce, somewhat paradoxically, the continuance of the rote and drill style of instruction. James' philosophy was conditioned by evolutionary concepts but, unlike his contemporary, Herbert Spencer, he maintained that the mind could exert creative control over the process of evolution. The function of education, he believed, was to foster good habits early in life in order to free the consciousness for higher human purposes. It is not difficult to see how undue emphasis on "fostering good habits" could be translated into a justification of instructional methods that differed little from discipline methods.

G. Stanley Hall: The Child and Adolescent. G. Stanley Hall is probably best known for his pioneering studies of adolescent psychology and his "General Psychonomic Law." The latter became the basis for a school of curriculum builders who were guided by its assertion that ontogeny recapitulates phylogeny, that is, that the development of the individual follows the same sequence as the development of the species. Although this idea has been largely discredited (Thorndike challenged it very quickly on the basis that what *is* found in phylogeny is a grossly inefficient guide to what *ought* to be emphasized in ontogeny), many of Hall's ideas were disseminated by his students, notably Terman and Gesell, and remain a significant force in elementary school curriculum thinking to the present day. The sequencing of curricular content was especially influenced by the developmental Child-Study movement fostered by Hall together with Freud in the decades immediately before and after World War I. Hall's impact on the *content* of curriculum was equally great inasmuch as the Child-Study trend gave considerable support to emphasis on the child's needs and interests as opposed to the former concern with schooling's formal content and purpose.

John Dewey: Social Reconstruction and Pragmatism. Dewey, of course, was the incomparable educational giant of his era. His thought generated a profound reform in educational theory and practice. Dewey, like Mann, saw the school as an important tool for social reconstruction. Viewing the serious problems of urban slums, rural poverty, and a host of other stresses generated by immigration and industrial growth, Dewey saw the school as the only agency which could take over educational functions being given up by the home and church. This view of the school as a legatee institution rapidly spread and opened up the curriculum to both new content and practices that far exceeded those which had been traditionally acceptable. Dewey's emphasis on pragmatism also had a deep effect on the content of curriculum. It especially accelerated the trend away from empty mind-exercising formalism and toward pragmatically meaningful emphasis in the selection of illustrations, exercises, and activities. He further influenced curricular reorganization by attacking the arbitrary division of the curriculum into isolated and unrelated subject areas. This criticism strongly encouraged the broad-fields theory of curriculum construction that emerged in the 1900's. Unfortunately, too many of Dewey's followers read him superficially or perhaps not at all. As a result, many abuses and malpractices flourished in his name. The loose organization of project method instruction together with objectives "democratically" determined too often gave rise to chaos in the name of spontaneity, shoddiness in place of scholarship, and triviality as a substitute for significant topics.

Edward Thorndike: The Birth of Scientism. Concurrent with the rise of the child-centered and pragmatic curriculum was the rapid rise of Scientism in education. It is in Edward Thorndike that we find the image of the scientist-educator *par excellence.* His confidence in the power of science to settle long-standing educational perplexities was simply unbounded. Through his stimulus-response (S-R) psychology, he influenced a generation of researchers, textbook authors, and classroom teachers. In spite of the fact that S-R psychology was rather quickly eclipsed by Gestalt psychology in the 1930's, Thorndike's experiments and ideas had been instrumental in disposing of faculty psychology as an effective force in the elementary school. His influence waxes prominently again today in the movement toward programed and computer-oriented instruction.

Arithmetic in the Early Progressive Era (1890-1930)

All three movements—Child-Study, Pragmatism, and Scientism—greatly modified the nature of the curriculum. Arithmetic content was abridged to allow more time for other subjects in the elementary school curriculum. At the primary grade level, systematic instruction in many instances actually terminated. In its place came a practice known as Incidentalism. Arithmetic instruction occurred only where a need for it occurred in connection with the other activities of the classroom. In 1922, Thorndike wrote, "It seems probable that little is gained by using any of the child's time for arithmetic before Grade 2, though there are many arithmetical facts he can learn before Grade 1. Postponement of systematic work in arithmetic to Grade 3 or even Grade 4 is allowable if better things are offered. . . . If, however, many children are to leave Grade 5 and 6 as now, we may think it wise to provide somehow that certain minima of arithmetic ability be given them."[3]

---

[3]Edward L. Thorndike, *The Psychology of Arithmetic* (New York: The Macmillan Company, 1922).

If Thorndike sounds a little uncertain in the use of the word "somehow" it is hardly surprising. Arithmetic instruction was rapidly heading toward an impasse of contradictory purposes and practices. As experience later indicated, incidental practice provided insufficient frequency of contact with arithmetic for the beginners to develop either basic skills or familiarity with fundamental facts. Even where systematic instruction was practiced, misplaced emphasis on Thorndike's Law of Exercise simply perpetuated the familiar rote and drill style of instruction. The companion Law of Effect, that successful achievement should be reinforced by the occurrence of some pleasant experience, defied practical application in such a situation.

The fact that the competency of teachers began to be measured by the extent to which their pupils secured mastery in speed and accuracy at grade level led to further frustration with arithmetic instruction. This pressure became especially prominent following the application of Social Utility Theory to curriculum construction. The idea involved was that curriculum should be scientifically constructed by restricting it to and basing it on only those facts and skills objectively found to be socially useful in the homes, shops, and factories of adult society. Its more ardent supporters held further that 100 per cent mastery of such "basic fundamentals" was the only goal with which a teacher could rest content. In the 1920's especially, scores of researchers set out to identify and tabulate this content. From such data, hundreds and for some subjects literally thousands of objectives were cataloged. Then, borrowing heavily from the prevalent concepts of child development, these objectives were assigned to certain grades according to the supposed needs, interests, and readiness of the children. The curriculum thus became one jaw of a vise in which the teacher was trapped. The other jaw was formed by the speed achievement tests which were increasingly regarded as a valid scientific measure of pupil mastery. Teachers and pupils alike were hard pressed between these opposing forces. Investigators uncovered the rueful statistic that, based even on a typical minimal standard of 70 per cent mastery, arithmetic was one of the leaders in the source of failures among elementary school subjects. Accordingly, its popularity declined to a new low.

Arithmetic in the Premodern Era (1930-1955)

The Age of Instructional Recipes. The two decades from 1930 to 1950 offered the elementary school a certain measure of respite from the reformers. In the face of economic depression and then world war, the public elementary school hardly seemed the key to the solution of urgent social problems as it had in the thinking of Mann and Dewey. In this relatively undisturbed state, attention of professional educators and teachers turned toward consolidating and stabilizing the principles and methods of instruction which had been advocated in such profusion during the preceding decades.

As always, the important methodological concern for arithmetic teachers centered on efficiently developing the pupils' computational proficiency. By about 1930, Thorndike's S-R psychology had been largely translated into arithmetic texts built on "unit skills."[4] If the essence of arithmetic instruction was bond formation, strengthening, and maintenance, then introduction of these bonds according to an hierarchical scheme seemed reasonable. Simple bonds were to be formed early; the more complex ones somewhat later in the child's development. This scheme also fitted nicely with the extensive grade-placement research[5] being conducted at this time. Finally, by stressing, especially in verbal problems, appropriate social applications (for example, if 2 pencils cost 5 cents, then . . . and so on), a well-mixed compromise of child-centered developmentalism, S-R psychology, Social Utility Theory, and Pragmatism was achieved.

Pupil performance, as measured by the rapidly expanding use of tests, continued to be disappointingly low, however. Naturally, many researchers turned their attention to finding instructional methods which would remedy this persistent malady. Various classroom techniques for teaching the fundamental operations were examined in the 1920's, 1930's, and 1940's.[6] This research laid the foundation for a rather voluminous arithmetic-methods literature containing highly specialized recipes for teaching particular skills and facts. By the end of the premodern period, numerous schools of thought had developed with little agreement between them. Excessive concern with one or another aspect of arithmetic instruction led to an emphasis on termi-

---

[4]See F. B. Knight, E. M. Luce, G. M. Ruch, *Problems in the Teaching of Arithmetic*; also L. J. Brueckner and Fred Kelly, "A Critical Evaluation of Methods of Analyzing Practice in Fractions," 29th Yearbook, National Society for the Study of Education, Part II, 1930, for a description of unit skills.

[5]C. W. Washburne, "Mental Age and the Arithmetic Curriculum," *Journal of Educational Psychology*, 23:210-31. Also in 38th Yearbook, National Society for the Study of Education, Part I, 1939, pp. 299-324; and 29th Yearbook, National Society for the Study of Education, Part II, 1930, Ch. 13.

[6]Probably the best of these is represented by W. A. Brownell and H. E. Moser, *Meaningful versus Mechanical Learning: A Study in Grade III Subtraction*, Duke University Research Studies in Education, No. 8 (Durham, N.C.: Duke University Press, 1949).

nology replete with abundant taboos. (For example, carrying, borrowing, rearranging, number "ending," bridging, "goes into," "is contained in," plus, and, take-away, subtract, constitute hardly the beginning of an endless list of terms from which certain selections would either be advocated for exclusive use or categorically banned depending on the authority or slogans one adopted.) Nevertheless, some stability in methods and terminology emerged in the arithmetic texts, often supported by extensive experimental findings. Perhaps the most striking example was the rapid increase in teaching subtraction by the "decomposition" method (rather than the "equal additions" or "Austrian" methods).

The Meaningful Method

A long-simmering controversy over rote versus meaningful instruction was for all intents and purposes settled in the 1930's. Thorndike, for instance, was one of many who had maintained that meaning simply got in the way of efficient computation and thus should be discussed only *after* computational mastery was achieved, if it should be discussed at all.[7] However, by the mid-1930's, research into the child's ability to transfer, generalize, and retain arithmetic information[8] suggested the superiority of meaningful instruction over rote processes relative to these variables. Experiments also refuted the claim that meaning caused reduced proficiency. In fact, no significant difference appeared between the methods in terms of resulting computational ability. In 1935, the official endorsement to meaningful instruction given by the National Council of Teachers of Mathematics[9] (NCTM) became the unchallenged guide to arithmetic instruction well into the 1950's. Unfortunately, much confusion resulted from an eager predisposition to use the word "meaningful" to refer to many things, so that in the 21st Yearbook of the National Council of Teachers of Mathematics, it was necessary to attempt to clarify the meaning of "meaning."[10] In general, however, meaningful instruction attempted to use techniques which would clarify the referents and make practical usage of the still hard to understand base-place value Arabic numera-

[7]Thorndike, *op. cit.*, 154.

[8]The classic study was done by C. Louis Thiele, *Contribution of Generalization to the Learning of the Addition Facts*, Contributions to Education, No. 673 (New York: Bureau of Publications, Teachers College, Columbia University, 1938).

[9]National Council of Teachers of Mathematics, Tenth Yearbook (The Council, 1935).

[10]National Council of Teachers of Mathematics, *The Learning of Mathematics, Its Theory and Practice,* 21st Yearbook (The Council, 1953).

tion system. Often, "meaningful" was inappropriately contrasted with "drill" rather than rote. As a result, drill was often reduced to dangerously low levels in the mistaken notion that it was not compatible with meaningful instruction.

The nearest thing to a national assessment of education that the United States has seen prior to the present time came about through mass testing during the two world wars. In 1942, Admiral Nimitz,[11] one of our highly respected military leaders, published a widely noted observation to the effect that the mathematical competence of freshmen entering college was critically low, even to the extent of hampering our war effort. Some eyes turned naturally toward the elementary as well as the high school to identify the culpable agency. A spate of research in the early 1940's substantiated the facts that (1) American pupils were unable to compete favorably with European children in mathematics, and (2) that, in general, mathematical proficiency of American high school graduates was intolerably low.[12] Because of the war, these reports did not have the impact that similar reports had following the shock of Sputnik some years later. In any case, little substantial change could be noted in elementary school arithmetic practices through the 1940's.

New Theories of Psychology and Curriculum. During the period from 1930 to 1950, two new psychologies rose to challenge the popular S-R theory. One was Gestalt psychology or Field Theory; the other was the rediscovered psychology of Piaget. To be sure, Freudian psychology and the Gesell school of child development had been prominent since the early 1920's, when Gestalt writings also began to appear. However, the translation of these two theories into textbook terminology was delayed largely until the end of World War II. At that time, synthesis of the several theories could be found in varying proportion depending on the text selected. Some, following Stokes,[13] for example, introduced ideas by using techniques for "differentiation [of the perceptual field] and an integration [into a generalized concept]." More pervasive was the recognition of Piagetian "stages" which led to an

---

[11]Admiral C. M. Nimitz, "The Importance of Mathematics in the War Effort," *The Mathematics Teacher,* February, 1942, pp. 88-89.

[12]See G. T. Buswell, "A Comparison of Achievement in Arithmetic in England and Central California," *The Arithmetic Teacher,* February, 1958, pp. 1-9; Klaas Kramer, "Arithmetic Achievement in Iowa and the Netherlands," *The Elementary School Journal,* February, 1959, pp. 258-63; and Jacob S. Orleans and Julia L. Sperling, "Arithmetic Knowledge of Graduate Students," *Journal of Educational Research,* 48:177-86, 1954.

[13]Claude N. Stokes, *Teaching the Meanings of Arithmetic* (New York: Appleton-Century-Crofts, Inc., 1951, p. 329).

almost universal revival of the popularity of "concrete" number experiences in the grades. The formal introduction to arithmetic via either
rote or meaningful counting gave way to some extent to concrete
experiences with cardinal numbers in the primary grades. Catherine
Stern's[14] *Structural Program* is the outstanding early example of a
complete concrete approach to arithmetic in the grades.

Some shifts in Social Utility Theory became evident toward the end
of this premodern period. Flournoy,[15] for instance, noted that mental
computation accounted for a large fraction of adult mathematics usage.
As a result of this and other similar observations, estimation and mental
computation gained considerable popularity and were given more
attention in the arithmetic textbooks.

By the mid-1950's, few teachers or parents anticipated any significant change in elementary school arithmetic instruction. In spite of
continuing evidence that all was not well, the corrective efforts of various individuals and groups received scant attention in the public mind.
A number of reports indicated that, despite the rhetoric of meaningful
theory, little evidence suggested that either teachers or pupils understood the meaning of much arithmetic content.[16] The grade placement
scheme, based largely on Washburne's research, also was challenged
by findings like those of Van Engen and Gibb[17] which demonstrated
important interactive effects between sequence and method of instruction. (This early finding would emerge later at the Wood's Hole Conference in a sweeping generalization that shattered all previous grade-
placement concepts: Any idea can be taught in an intellectually
legitimate form to children of any age!)[18] Thus, the principles by
which arithmetic content was sequenced appeared to be resting on
crumbling foundations. However, the scope of arithmetic instruction
had remained largely unchanged for nearly two centuries and classroom methodology had become remarkably uniform for nearly two
decades under the aegis of meaningful theory. Change, if it could be
expected at all, certainly seemed to be coming in slow and carefully

---

[14]Catherine Stern, *Children Discover Arithmetic* (New York: Harper and
Brothers, 1949).

[15]M. Frances Flournoy, "The Effectiveness of Instruction in Mental Arithmetic,"
Elementary School Journal, 55:148-153, November, 1954.

[16]V. J. Glennon, "Testing Meanings in Arithmetic," *Arithmetic,* 1949, Supplementary Educational Monographs, No. 70 (Chicago: University of Chicago Press).

[17]Henry Van Engen and Glenadine Gibb, *General Mental Functions Associated
with Division,* Educational Service Studies, No. 2 (Cedar Falls: Iowa State
Teachers College, 1956).

[18]Jerome S. Bruner, *The Process of Education* (Cambridge: Harvard University
Press, 1961).

measured steps. And that, more than any other single reason, is why the happenings of the late 1950's had the traumatic effect of a revolution on so many parents and teachers. Change was, indeed, unexpected!

The Modern Era (1950-   )

Current Reform Trends

Looking back over the panorama of educational change one can identify two highly significant events which dominated the course of subsequent reform. The first of these was the effort by the advocates of universal education to secure necessary political support by vesting control of the schools in local units of government. This move was the decisive factor in attaining, after an arduous struggle, free and mandatory schooling for all children. It also directly caused the second great event. By the late 1800's political corruption at the local level was widely noted. The appointments of superintendents, teachers, and principals lay at the mercy of political patronage. The larger school budgets, inadequately controlled, stimulated graft. Badly needed school buildings provided many with extra income via artificially inflated construction costs. When Rice and others exposed this situation, the natural remedy seemed to lie in taking control from the hands of the corrupt politicians and vesting it in the rising class of professional educators, a class popularized dramatically by the founding of Teachers College at Columbia University in 1887.

As matters turned out, control was not taken from one group and given to the other but rather a better balance was achieved between local lay control of the policies and purposes of the schools and professional control of the techniques and practices by which these objectives were effected. Nevertheless, this combination proved inadequate to the task of providing a satisfactory education for the children in grades K-12. The schools, in spite of efforts to bring scientific techniques to bear on the control of capricious innovation, were severely afflicted by an addiction to fads, slogans, and superficial implementation of philosophical and psychological principles. Research resulted not in the control of these excesses but often served to amplify harmful effects through the introduction of a hair-splitting pseudoscientific argot, dubbed "Educanto" by Koerner,[19] and through the proliferation

---

[19]James D. Koerner, *The Miseducation of Teachers* (Boston: Houghton Mifflin, 1963).

of schools of methodological thought contending with each other for the allegiance of the teacher. The net result was a disenchantment with the power of science to solve educational problems.[20] This effect was noticeable already in the mid-1930's. In the confusion which followed the collapse of scientific authority, classroom practice adapted by reverting to the cautious and conservative stance epitomized in the motto "Be not the first by which the new is tried nor yet the last to lay the old aside." In the case of arithmetic, the old consisted of a predisposition to emphasis on drill and, accentuated by the grade teacher's superficial grasp of mathematics content, rote rather than meaningful instruction, all slogans to the contrary notwithstanding.

To be sure, progress had been made. Educational opportunity had been vastly expanded to include citizens of all ages; instruction had become more humane and sensitive to needs of children; teachers' professional status had grown from the Lancastrian low through the phase of normal schooling to recent high standards of a full-fledged undergraduate college education; sophisticated administrative techniques were implemented for handling the astronomical number of students and dollars required by modern education; and measures to assess some aspects of intelligence, ability, and personality had been constructed. Nevertheless, inadequate levels of attainment continued to be observed in the graduates of our grade and high schools, especially in fields which were of growing importance to the sustenance of this nation's position as a major industrial power.[21]

Thus in the last decade, curriculum reform has been dominated by the so-called "pursuit of excellence." Once again, the same kind of forces were set in motion which earlier brought about a better balance between political and professional control of the schools. This time, since it appeared that curriculum and instruction had become imbalanced by *professional* biases at the expense of academic excellence, the significant shift has been toward a larger role for academic specialists in curriculum development. This shift has been most notable in the sciences, which were the first to receive direct attention, the languages, and, most recently, social studies. Extrapolating past experience, we might expect that this trend will stabilize in a more effective balance of control and contributions by government, professional administrators and educators, and academic specialists. Not to

---

[20]National Society for the Study of Education, *The Scientific Movement in Education,* Thirty-seventh Yearbook (The Society, 1938). Cf. also, Thirty-eighth National Society for the Study of Education Yearbook, Part II, p. 488.

[21]Torsten Husen (ed.), *International Study of Achievement in Mathematics,* Vols. I and II (New York: John Wiley and Sons, 1967).

be ignored, since it has been traditionally a pervasive force in patterns of school operation, is the business community—including both industry and labor. In short, the American school system is passing through its adolescence with the usual kinds of difficulties. What sort of mature form it takes depends to a large extent on the effectiveness with which the various legitimate contributors to its successful performance are harnessed into a functioning unit. How successful that harnessing will be remains to be seen.

For better or worse, these forces are shaping the schools which the teachers being prepared today will teach in tomorrow. The implications of these apparent trends for those who will be teaching mathematics in the grades comprise in large part the subject of this book.

HISTORICAL SKETCH OF THE DEVELOPMENT OF MATHEMATICS

Introduction

As Conant has pointed out in his book, *The Education of American Teachers,* an ill-concealed hostility has existed between academic specialists and professional educators almost from the inception of the class of professional educators. With rare exceptions, constructive communication between the two groups has been until recent years virtually nonexistent. It is not surprising therefore that mathematics, as the academic specialist in mathematics understands it, could become almost completely unrelated to what was taught as arithmetic or mathematics in the elementary and secondary schools. This is, in effect, what has happened. The school curriculum, left to the direction of well-intentioned but misdirected purposes established by many whose grasp of mathematics was superficial at best, simply went its own way and drifted completely out of the mainstream of mathematical thought.

To appreciate this situation fully would require at this point a digression into the historical development of mathematics. We must of necessity leave the details to the interested reader[22] and sketch here the very high points of the startling and profound progress in mathematics in the last four centuries; indeed, the astounding expansion of

[22]See D. E. Smith, *History of Mathematics,* Vols. I and II (New York: Dover, 1923); Dirk J. Struik, *A Concise History of Mathematics* (New York: Dover, 1948); Howard Eves, *An Introduction to the History of Mathematics* (New York: Holt, Rinehart and Winston, 1964); Lucienne Felix, *The Modern Aspect of Mathematics* (New York: Basic Books, Inc., 1960); E. T. Bell, *Mathematics, Queen and Servant of Science* (New York: McGraw-Hill Book Company, Inc., 1951).

the field in the last 50 years. This remarkable performance is without parallel in human history and exists today with its vigor undiminished. Little wonder that the mathematicians, once interested in the problems of school mathematics instruction, were astonished at the pallid shadow of their dynamic field found in the schools.

From Ancient Times to the Renaissance

The growth of mathematics as an intellectual discipline can be traced back into antiquity. The Babylonian, Egyptian, Greek, and Roman civilizations possessed remarkably well-developed mathematical structures. Portions of this development have been found as early as the beginning of the second millenium B.C. Most notable was the work of the great Greek mathematicians Pythagoras, Euclid, and Archimedes. During the Golden Age of Greece, mathematical rigor in the form of deductive proof first made its significant appearance as an important part of mathematics.

Following the fall of the Roman Empire, most important mathematical activity took place in the East. There the base ten place-value scheme which we use today for naming numbers was developed —the so-called Hindu-Arabic system. Along with this new notation came the development of novel computational schemes transmitted to the West via the arithmetic of al-Khwarizmi, which when Latinized became the "algorithm" of our modern mathematical language. Another significant development from India during this period of the European Dark Ages was the "Hisab al-jabr wal-mugabala" or science of equations. Thus, al-jabr or algebra came to us as a term referring to a much more restricted area of mathematics than it now serves. Importantly, Arabic algebra and Greek geometry were sharply contrasted by the fact that the latter had a well-developed axiomatic foundation which the former lacked. The different origins show clearly in American secondary mathematics courses up to the present time, algebra being treated largely as an empirical science of manipulating equations and geometry taught deductively from Euclid's axioms.

Mathematics in Western Europe languished as the large-scale economy of the Roman Empire vanished. There is little evidence of mathematical activity to report in the years between about 500 and 1000 A.D., beyond the calculation of the dates of Easter. Interestingly, a courtier of Charlemagne named Alcuin is known for his collection of ancient "Problems for the Quickening of the Mind" which apparently influenced textbook writers for centuries afterward. (For example, a dog chasing a rabbit, which has a start of 150 feet, jumps 9 feet every time the rabbit jumps 7. In how many leaps does the dog overtake the rabbit?) Among other things, such problems indicated the emancipation of mathematics from purely utilitarian concerns.

During the five centuries between 1000 and 1500 A.D., Western mathematics made slow recovery, accelerating as centers of commerce and national states emerged in Europe. By the beginning of the seventeenth century, computational techniques had been raised to new heights under the stimulation of advances in commerce, surveying, navigation, astronomy, and military engineering. The general cubic and biquadratic equations had been solved; negative numbers and imaginary numbers were treated with some sophistication; and in the computational spirit of the time, logarithms were invented.

From Renaissance to Industrial Revolution

In the period from about 1450 to 1750, answers to questions concerning the cause of motion raised by Aristotle (384-322 B.C.) began to become clear. In astronomy, Copernicus (born in 1473) had the inspiration to shift the origin of the observational frame of reference from the earth's center to the sun's center. The resulting simplification in point of view enabled Kepler, a century later, to fit three equations to the empirical data gathered over a lifetime by his teacher, Tycho Brahe. While this success delighted Kepler, it provided only a mathematical *description* of planetary motion. The *cause* of motion still remained a mystery. However, Galileo was simultaneously working on the causes of terrestrial motion. And his blend of experiment and reasoning yielded evidence of a property he called inertia. This discovery meant that, contrary to the authority of Aristotle, motion can occur without force. The resulting attempt to find a common cause for both terrestrial and astronomical motion was instrumental in stimulating the invention of the calculus. This powerful form of mathematical analysis was simultaneously invented by Newton and Leibniz in a brief period preceding 1700. Modern-day evidence of the power of these methods is given dramatically by the accomplishments of our space program, which, as the illustration shows, was anticipated by Newton 300 years ago.

Not only were new forms of mathematics being invented, but the ancient forms were undergoing change as well. In the early 1600's, Descartes, whose name is connected with the now familiar Cartesian coordinates, contributed not only to the development of the calculus but also to the unification of geometry and algebra. A number of mathematicians of this time, besides Descartes, were interested in what is now called analytic geometry. Among them was Fermat whose

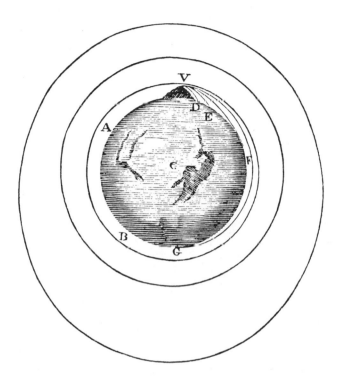

Illustration 4

A *drawing from Newton's* System of the World *(attached to later editions of the* Principa*) showing what would happen if an object were projected from a high mountain with various speeds. Newton showed that if the speed were great enough, the object would not "come down" but would continue to circle the earth in an elliptical orbit.*

contributions to number theory are among those topics now appearing in some modern elementary school mathematics textbooks. Pascal also contributed to the development of the calculus and together with Fermat founded the mathematical theory of probability. Although motivated at first by consultant services to gamblers and later by an emerging interest in actuarial problems raised by the development of insurance, topics from this branch of mathematics are now considered appropriate for inclusion in the modern mathematics curriculum.[23] Another landmark of the 1600's is the work of Desargues who began

---

[23]Cambridge Conference on School Mathematics, *Goals for School Mathematics* (Boston: Houghton Mifflin, 1963), p. 9.

the process of setting geometry free from domination by Euclid. But the monumental work of the century was the nearly simultaneous and independent discovery of a general method of differentiation and integration as inverse processes by Newton and Leibniz. Using the new calculus, Newton unified the science of mechanics with his sweeping inverse-square law of gravitation, explaining at one stroke such seemingly diverse phenomena as the falling apple, the motion of the moon, the tides, and heliocentric planetary motion.

The eighteenth century was a period of much excitement in applying the powerful new tool of the calculus to mechanics. This emphasis on applications gave rise to the later split between applied and pure mathematics. (In Europe, children today take "maths" rather than "math." The plural form reflects the feeling that applied and pure mathematics are two different things. In this country, the split is downgraded.)[24] The eighteenth century was marked by its headlong abandonment of logical rigor both in creating and applying mathematics. The inclination was to ignore the seemingly impractical cautions raised now and then about the logical foundations on which practice was being built. Indeed, success seemed to be its own validation of mathematical process. And evidence of success was everywhere to be seen as the technical foundations of the industrial revolution were being laid.

Creative mathematics was not abandoned to be sure, but logical rigor was swept aside in the rush to apply results. Perhaps the most fertile creator of mathematics of all time was Leonhard Euler who lived during this era. Today one finds in elementary texts his discovery of the relation between the number of vertices (V), edges (E), and faces (F) of a closed polyhedron ($V + F - E = 2$) and certain well-known mathematical recreations with a topological flavor such as the Koningsberg bridge problem.[25]

Toward the end of the century, progress had been so extensive that Lagrange wrote to D'Alembert, "Doesn't it seem to you that there is some trend toward decadence already in the field of mathematics?" It seemed that between Euler and D'Alembert everything mathematically worthwhile had been discovered.

The explosive beginning of the nineteenth century, with its great revolutions, both political and industrial, put a quick end to such pessimism. The ideological break with the past stimulated the growth of the physical sciences as well as mathematics, created new classes of

---

[24]Cf. CCSM, *op. cit.,* p. 11.
[25]Edwin E. Moise and Floyd L. Downs, *Geometry* (Reading, Mass.: Addison-Wesley, 1964), p. 298.

$$V + F - E = 2$$

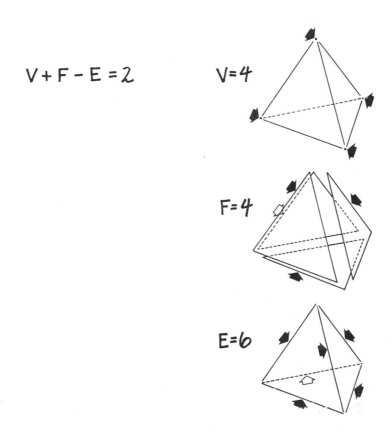

$$V = 4$$

$$F = 4$$

$$E = 6$$

Illustration 5

The polyhedron, illustrating Euler's Law: $V + F - E = 2$.

people interested in both science and technical education, and caused a major reform in the schools and universities. Out of this change grew a tremendous outpouring of mathematical creation. So great was the expansion of knowledge that we see for the first time the emergence of specialists, first broadly grouped as "pure" or "applied" mathematicians, then as algebrists, analysts, geometers, statisticians, and the like. One of the last encyclopedic minds was the incomparable C. F. Gauss. A brief catalog of his contributions includes the greatest advance in number theory since the days of Euclid, the method of least squares, differential geometry, the theory of complex numbers, and non-Euclidean geometry.

The creative mathematicians of the 1800's simply are too numerous to mention, let alone do justice to. We content ourselves with the note that among the more important events was the concern once again with mathematical rigor. This concern had been lost in the excitement of the previous two centuries as mathematicians rushed to secure practical results offered by the amazing new tools of their trade.

In the nineteenth century it increasingly occurred to many that the whole mathematical edifice was in danger of imminent collapse due to logically inadequate foundations. Paradoxes which had seemed unimportant in the past now loomed large on the horizon as fundamental obstacles to progress. But through the work of men like Gauss, Abel, Bolzano, Galois, and Cauchy, rigorous foundations for the calculus and modern algebra were established during this period. These ideas served as powerful conceptual tools for unifying various branches of mathematics and ultimately served to stimulate a new burst of mathematical creativity in the late nineteenth and twentieth centuries. Perhaps the most important influence on modern mathematics came about through the work of Reimann (1826-1866) who not only liberated geometry completely from the Euclidean yoke but invented a unifying principle which permitted the classification of all existent forms of geometry as well as the creation of any number of new kinds of geometry. Directly as a result of Reimann, topology, for instance, received impetus for its rapid growth in recent years.

The Golden Age of Mathematics (1900-   )

Problems in the logical foundations of mathematics led to a search for a primitive, consistent, theoretical basis on which all mathematics could be built. Although this ideal has not been achieved, indeed cannot be, the search led to an increasingly greater sense of unity among the various branches of mathematics. With Cantor's expansion of set theory[26] and the subsequent exhaustive treatment of logic by Whitehead and Russell,[27] an epic perspective of the mathematical domain became evident in the early twentieth century. Viewed in simplified terms, the modern picture shows mathematics based on the foundation stone of set theory and logic. From this basis rise the twin pillars of abstract algebra and topology which support the whole of mathematical activity.[28] For those capable of scaling the intellectual peaks, the view of the mathematical world is not only breathtaking

---

[26]G. Cantor, *Contributions to the Founding of the Theory of Transfinite Numbers* (New York: Dover).

[27]A. N. Whitehead and B. Russell, *Principia Mathematica* (Cambridge, 1912).

[28]Felix, *op. cit.*

but commands eager exploration of new vistas opening up in every direction.

THE CONFLUENCE OF MATHEMATICS
AND THE MATHEMATICS CURRICULUM (1950-   )

Modern Mathematics and the Schools

On the basis of the unified view of their domain attained in the last four centuries, and especially the last half-century, mathematicians once interested in the school curriculum were naturally eager to see the nature, spirit, and excitement of their work conveyed to the children in the grades. The essence of their recommendations, at the elementary level, has been to modify the disproportionate emphasis on numeration systems and computational algorithms in favor of increased attention to mathematical *ideas*. Hopefully, the child entering junior high school would then be adequately prepared for much more rapid progress into significant mathematical activity. In order to achieve this preparation, the former compartmentalization of mathematics into arithmetic, algebra, and geometry has been abandoned. In its place, selections from certain fundamental areas of mathematics— logic, sets, real numbers, and geometry—are being urged for implementation into a systematic program of premathematics instruction in the grades, to be followed by an axiomatic development at the junior high and high school levels.

If the peaks of mathematical attainment are an arduous challenge to the mathematically naive, the descent to the levels of elementary school arithmetic is not without its hazards for the sophisticated mathematician. Some recent classroom experiments by the academic specialists have been less than blazing successes, the result of stumbling over those obstacles characteristic of the immature mind which are quick to trip any who give sole attention to content.[29] Here is a case in point where the joint work of content specialists and classroom teachers would be most fruitful. The problem of establishing reliable lines of communication between the two levels is as difficult as it is important. Certainly the task has barely begun.

---

[29]Cf. accounts of initial attempts to implement CCSM recommendations in the classroom, mimeographed reports from Educational Services Incorporated, Watertown, Mass. For example, one experimentalist was startled to find young children base their chip trading on preference for one color over another rather than on the basis of blue = 10, red = 5, white = 1.

Implementing Modern Mathematics Curricula

In 1952, a committee at the University of Illinois (later called UICSM) began looking into the matter to see what could be done to raise the ability of high school graduates to understand and pursue modern mathematics at the college level. It soon became apparent that both elementary and high school programs would have to be drastically revised to bring them from an essentially medieval orientation to that of the present era. In 1955, the Commission on Mathematics[30] published a set of recommendations to guide the first steps secondary schools could take to come of modern mathematical age. These suggestions were subsequently implemented by the School Mathematics Study Group in the form of experimental materials which were to serve as models for a new generation of textbooks. Commercial publishers were wary of radical change, however, and change in the standard algebra and geometry textbooks was evolutionary rather than revolutionary.

Following the national humiliation in 1957 by the Russian launching of Sputnik, education (through its ability to augment the supply of scientists especially) was once again linked powerfully to the nation's destiny. Mathematics study groups, such as University of Maryland Mathematics Project and Ball State, flourished at many universities and colleges. Some school districts also initiated the development of new curricula. Foremost among these was the Greater Cleveland Mathematics Project. Throughout the land the phrase "modern mathematics" suddenly was on everyone's lips.

At first, teachers were as much mystified as parents. But as training programs were begun, and the first conservative alterations appeared in the textbooks, some sense of relief was gained. The new mathematics really wasn't so different, or so it seemed: a new emphasis on sets and various numeration systems, a renewed emphasis on discovery methods and concrete materials, a continuation of the rhetoric over problem solving, some talk about structural principles and unifying ideas, but apparently nothing astonishingly different. Many teachers could point to having been through similar phases before. (After all, Stern's system of instruction was called "*structural* arithmetic;" the meaningful method had stressed "understanding" and "generalization;" all good teachers sought to develop insight into "patterns" and "relationships.") Some conviction even held that this was just another fad that would soon go the way of most attempts at reform.

---

[30]The Report of the Commission on Mathematics, College Entrance Examination Board, 1959, Vol. I, *Program for College Preparatory Mathematics.*

By 1963, a group of academicians meeting at Cambridge noted the tendency toward crystalization of the small progress that had been made since the mid-1950's. They recognized that the scarcity of adequately trained teachers would require that future work be done within the framework of the "classical" curriculum, and inferentially, that progress would be slow. Nevertheless, in response to the need to implement more radical revisions than any so far made public, a bold new set of mathematics objectives was formulated—the most ambitious and startling set of recommendations yet proposed.[31] This report, for all its sharp contrast in pedagogical naivete and mathematical sophistication, constitutes the most recent measure of the gap which separates curricular aspiration and achievement in the teaching of school mathematics.

Inevitably, as mathematics changes and the needs of society continue to change, the school programs and the mathematics curriculum will respond in like manner. The changes which have come about in the recent past are being perpetuated through the work of several experimental projects, some of which have already been mentioned. The classroom teacher must be aware of the people, places, and purposes connected with these groups. Table 1 is a brief summary of the facts relating to the most influential experimental projects which have influenced curricular change especially in the last decade.[32]

Conclusion

Some immediate conclusions can be drawn from this historical survey. Certainly the modern mathematics-reform movement is not a fad or temporary preoccupation with novel mathematics approaches. It validly reflects the continual need to change educational programs to keep them in line with the developing state of knowledge in the field as well as the needs of society. One of the most urgent needs to effect this change is an increase in the supply of skilled elementary school teachers. Certainly a major effort is underway to resolve this problem.

---

[31]CCSM, *Goals for School Mathematics*, pp. 31-41.

[32]Further information on these projects is available through the project directors. For a complete list of national and international projects now concerned with K-12 mathematics and science curriculum, see J. David Lockard, *Report of the International Clearinghouse on Science and Mathematics Curricular Developments, 1967* (College Park, Md.: American Association for the Advancement of Science and the Science Teaching Center, University of Maryland, May, 1967); and Edwina Deans, *Elementary School Mathematics: New Directions*. Bulletin 1963, No. 13 (Washington, D.C.: U.S. Department of Health, Education, and Welfare, Office of Education, 1963).

Table 1

Developmental Mathematics Curriculum Projects

Name of Project	Director and Address	Began	Summary of Basic Purposes
School Mathematics Study Group (SMSG)	E. G. Begle Cedar Hall Stanford U. Stanford, California	1959*	1. To provide a curriculum based on mathematics rather than social applications. 2. To develop courses of study, teaching materials; to promote inservice education. 3. To emphasize precision of language, knowledge and appreciation of mathematical systems.
*Conference on elementary school mathematics.			
Greater Cleveland Mathematics Program	Dr. G. H. Baird Greater Cleveland Research Council 75 Public Square Cleveland 11, Ohio	1959	1. The logical and systematic presentation of arithmetic to all children that will enable them to understand basic mathematical concepts before being taught computational schemes.
University of Illinois Arithmetic Project (UIAP)	Dr. David Page 887 Commonwealth Avenue Newton, Massachusetts	1958	1. To devise materials to help children view work in mathematics as a fascinating adventure. 2. To stimulate curiosity, exploration, experimentation, and discovery.
Madison Project of Syracuse University and Webster College	Dr. R. B. Davis Smith Hall Syracuse University Syracuse, New York	1957	1. To revitalize the teacher education program in mathematics. 2. To develop, disseminate, and implement a supplementary program for nursery school through grade 12.
Minnesota Mathematics and Science Teaching Project (MINNEMAST) (Initially: Prof. Paul Rosenbloom)	Dr. James H. Werntz, Jr. 720 Washington Ave. S.E. Minneapolis, Minnesota	1961	1. To produce a curriculum based on what children can learn; prepare teachers to teach it. 2. Emphasis on mathematical structure for its own sake as well as strong emphasis on applications.
University of Maryland Mathematics Project (UMMaP)	Prof. John R. Mayor College of Education University of Maryland College Park, Maryland	1957	1. To contribute to improved teaching of mathematics. 2. To produce experimental textbooks for JHS and mathematics textbooks for elementary school teachers

Table 1—Continued

Name of Project	Director and Address	Began	Summary of Basic Purposes
Stanford Project	Prof. Patrick Suppes Ventura Hall Stanford University Stanford, California	1959	3. To develop inservice courses. 1. To develop an elementary mathematics program from the notion of sets and operations on sets. 2. To develop a program of geometry for the primary and intermediate grades. 3. To assess an experimental project on logic for grades 5 and 6, designed for the academically gifted.
Computer-Based Mathematics Instruction	Prof. Patrick Suppes Ventura Hall Stanford University Stanford, California	1963	1. To provide a controlled environment for psychological and pedagogical studies of learning. 2. Drill and practice in elementary mathematics: mathematical logic for grades.
Cambridge Conference on School Mathematics	Mr. Hugh P. Bradley Educational Services, Inc. 55 Chapel Street Newton, Massachusetts	1963	1. To explore curriculum reform needs in mathematics with a view to the long-range future.
Patterns in Arithmetic	Dr. Henry Van Engen R&D Center for Learning 1404 Regent Street Madison, Wisconsin	1964	1. The development of a self-contained mathematics program to be used in classroom units for instruction and teacher training.
Project Mathematique de Sherbrooke	Prof. Zoltan P. Dienes 1382 rue Dominion Sherbrooke Province de Quebec Canada	1965	1. Emphasis on structure of the foundations of mathematics; laboratory work with classroom work; concrete experiences in varied situations; logic started as soon as the child comes to school.

The changing mathematics program is not limited to the grades, of course. As change is made at one level, it permits or perhaps necessitates change at the preceding or following levels. One of the predictable effects of this perturbation of the curriculum will be a broader range of topics and skills taught in elementary and secondary mathematics programs.[33] Although present requirements are still largely influenced by the policies resulting from the work of the Committee of Fifteen at the turn of the century, it is reasonable to expect that the fairly uniform mathematics curriculum will become a thing of the past. A glance at Table 1, especially the column labeled "Summary of Basic Purposes," indicates a sample of the wide variety of experimental approaches being tried to update school mathematics programs. There is little reason to expect the range of innovation to decrease in the near future. Indeed, the report of the Cambridge Conference on School Mathematics[34] (CCSM) indicates a *broadening* of the possible approaches which may be used to build the new programs. All of this means for the elementary school, in particular, the need to continue to work diligently through inservice and other means toward cooperative progress with the academic specialists who are fueling this reform.

The present period has been described as one in which Nobel Prize winners discover John Dewey. If this is so, teachers can well afford to assist the academicians in this discovery in exchange for subject matter assistance. An essential goal of current efforts must be the promotion of cooperation between teachers and academicians in order more effectively to attain the curricular objectives for which both are striving.

Topics for Further Investigation

1. Trace the nature of change in elementary-level arithmetic textbooks with respect to one of the following criteria: (a) nature or type of content emphasized; (b) view of the importance of mathematics in society; (c) view of the importance of mathematics to the child; (d) psychological basis for organizing the text; (e) trends in grade placement of topics, or if very early texts are included, the intended age of the learner; (f) amount of freedom for the teacher to deviate from the text; (g) amount of class time expected to be spent on arithmetic; (h) amount of drill required; (i) kind of organization (rule, example, exercise; examples, rule, exercise; examples, explanation, rule, drill; and the like).

---

[33]Cf. Chapter 4.
[34]CCSM, *op. cit.*, Sections 5 and 6.

2. Trace the argument for rote versus meaningful instruction. Did *meaningful* refer to the same thing in the 1930's that mathematicians signify by the term in the 1960's? What are the three kinds of meaning Van Engen describes in the 21st NCTM Yearbook?

3. Trace the cycling back and forth between the opposing points of view (a) that the child should be adjusted to existing social institutions and (b) that man should struggle to adapt social institutions to his needs—as it has affected the nature of mathematics instruction over the years. Try to build a case for describing the present situation. What *is* the view at present? What was it in 1950? (Cf. 16, 17, 18, 26 NSSE Yearbooks for an anti-Deweyian view of the role of the school in social reform.)

4. In what ways do the recommendations of mathematicians today seem to coincide with the tenets of Progressivism as expounded by Dewey, Kilpatrick, and others? How do they differ from the views of the Social Utility Theorists of the 1920's and 1930's?

5. Take a position and defend it with respect to the place of drill and memorization in the mathematics curriculum today. Do you agree with the CCSM comments on the top of page 8 in *Goals for School Mathematics* describing the "only way" to impart technical skills? What do they mean by saying that "adequate practice *can* be given along with more mathematics"? How will that save time as they assert on the bottom of page 7?

6. What do you think about the relative influence of marks and college-entrance requirements on the mathematics curriculum as opposed to say the ideal of building a mathematically literate citizenry? To what extent are the educational policies of 1900 still active forces in the curriculum?

7. A basic question of curriculum construction is concerned with what knowledge is of most worth. What is the real worth of mathematics in an advanced industrial society such as ours today? Do you think it deserves more time in the curriculum today (or less, or is it about right)? How would you rank mathematics study in order of importance with other subjects now commonly taught in the elementary school?

Bibliography

Ball, W. W. *A Short Account of the History of Mathematics.* The Macmillan Company, 1888.

Beberman, Max. *An Emerging Program of Secondary School Mathematics.* Cambridge: Harvard University Press, 1958.

Bell, E. T. *Mathematics, Queen and Servant of Science.* New York: McGraw-Hill Book Company, Inc., 1951.

————. *Men of Mathematics.* New York: McGraw-Hill Book Company, Inc.

————. *The Development of Mathematics.* McGraw-Hill Book Company, Inc., 1940.

Bergamini, David, *et al. Mathematics.* Life Science Library, 1963.

Brownell, W. *Arithmetic in Grade I and II.* Durham, N.C.: Duke University Press, 1941.

————. "The Place of Meaning in the Teaching of Arithmetic," *The Elementary School Journal,* January, 1947, pp. 156-65.

Brownell, W., and G. Hendrickson. "How Children Learn Information, Concepts, and Generalizations," *Learning and Instruction.* 49th Yearbook, Part I, NSSE, 1950, pp. 92-128.

Brownell, W., and H. E. Moser. *Meaningful versus Mechanical Learning: A Study in Grade III Subtraction.* Duke University Research Studies in Education, No. 8. Durham, N.C.: Duke University Press, 1949.

Brueckner, L., and F. Grossnickle. *How To Make Arithmetic Meaningful.* Winston, 1947.

Brueckner, L., and Fred Kelly. "A Critical Evaluation of Methods of Analyzing Practice in Fractions," 29th Yearbook, National Society for the Study of Education, Part II, 1930.

Bruner, J. S. "On Learning Mathematics," *The Mathematics Teacher,* December, 1960.

————. *The Process of Education.* Cambridge: Harvard University Press, 1961.

————. *Toward a Theory of Instruction.* Cambridge: Belknap Press of Harvard University Press, 1966.

Buswell, G. T. "A Comparison of Achievement in Arithmetic in England and Central California," *The Arithmetic Teacher,* February, 1958, pp. 1-9.

Cajori, Florian. *A History of Elementary Mathematics.* New York: The Macmillan Company, 1921.

Cambridge Conference on School Mathematics. *Goals for School Mathematics.* Boston: Houghton Mifflin, 1963.

Cantor, G. *Contributions to the Founding of the Theory of Transfinite Numbers.* Dover Publications, Inc., (CA. 1915).

Commission on Mathematics, *Program for College Preparatory Mathematics.* College Entrance Examination Board, 1959. Vol. I.

Commission on Post-War Plans. "The Second Report of the Commission on Post-War Plans," *The Mathematics Teacher,* 38:195-220, May, 1945.

Committee on the Undergraduate Program in Mathematics. "Recommendations of the Mathematical Association of America for the Training of Teachers of Mathematics," *The Mathematics Teacher,* 53:632-638, 1960.

Conant, James B. *The Education of American Teachers.* New York: McGraw-Hill, 1963.

Cremins, Lawrence A. *The Transformation of the School.* New York: Alfred A. Knopf, 1961.

Dawson, D., and A. Reddell. "The Case for the Meaning Theory in Teaching Arithmetic," *Elementary School Journal,* LV, March, 1955, pp. 393-399.

Deans, E. *Elementary School Mathematics: New Directions.* Washington, D.C.: Office of Education, 1963.

————. *New Mathematics Programs.* Washington, D.C.: National Council of Teachers of Mathematics, 1963.

————. *The Growth of Mathematical Ideas, Grades K-12.* 24th Yearbook of the NCTM. Washington, D.C.: The Council, 1959.

DeVault, M. Vere (ed.). *Improving Mathematics Programs.* Columbus: Charles E. Merrill Books, Inc., 1961.

Dewey, John. *How We Think.* Boston: D. C. Heath, 1933.

Eby, Frederick. *The Development of Modern Education.* Englewood Cliffs, N.J.: Prentice-Hall, Inc., 1932.

Eves, Howard. *An Introduction to the History of Mathematics.* New York: Holt, Rinehart and Winston, 1964.

————. "A History—or—Mathematics Time Strip," *The Mathematics Teacher,* Vol. LIV, 6:452-454, October, 1961.

Felix, Lucienne. *The Modern Aspect of Mathematics.* New York: Basic Books, Inc., 1960.

Flournoy, M. Frances. "The Effectiveness of Instruction in Mental Arithmetic," *Elementary School Journal,* 55:148-153, November, 1954.

Glennon, V. J. "Testing Meanings in Arithmetic," *Arithmetic,* 1949, Supplementary Educational Monographs, No. 70. Chicago: University of Chicago Press.

Harap, H., and C. Mapes. "The Learning of Fundamentals in an Arithmetic Activity Program," *Elementary School Journal,* 34:515-25, 134.

Harris, Chester W. (ed.). *Encyclopedia of Educational Research,* 3rd edition. New York: The Macmillan Company, 1960.

Houston, W. R., and M. V. DeVault. "Mathematics In-Service Education: Teacher Growth Increases Pupil Growth," *The Arithmetic Teacher,* IX, May, 1963, pp. 243-47.

Howard, Charles F. "Three Methods of Teaching Arithmetic," *California Journal of Educational Research,* I, January, 1950, pp. 3-7.

Husen, Torsten (ed.). *International Study of Achievement in Mathematics,* Vols. I and II. New York: John Wiley and Sons, 1967.

Jarvis, Oscar T. "Time Allotment Relationships to Pupil Achievement in Arithmetic," *The Arithmetic Teacher,* May, 1963, pp. 248-50.

Kemeny, J. G., *et al. New Directions in Mathematics.* Englewood Cliffs, N.J.: Prentice-Hall, 1963.

Kline, Morris. *Mathematics in Western Culture.* New York: Oxford University Press, 1953.

Knight, F. B., E. M. Luse, and G. M. Ruch. *Problems in the Teaching of Arithmetic.* Iowa City, Iowa, 1924.

Koerner, James D. *The Miseducation of American Teachers.* Baltimore: Penguin Books, 1963.

Kramer, Klaas. "Arithmetic Achievement in Iowa and the Netherlands," *The Elementary School Journal,* February, 1959, pp. 258-63.

Lockard, J. David. *Report of the International Clearinghouse on Science and Mathematics Curricular Developments, 1967.* College Park, Md.: American Association for the Advancement of Science and the Science Teaching Center, University of Maryland, May, 1967.

Mathematics Association of America. *Course Guides for the Training of Teachers of Elementary School Mathematics,* CUPM, Berkeley, California, P. O. Box 1024, July, 1964.

Mathematics in General Education. (PEA Report) Report of the Commission on Mathematics of the Progressive Education Association. Appleton-Century Co., 1940.

Mayer, Martin. *The Schools.* New York: Harper Brothers, 1961.

McMurray, C. *Special Method in Arithmetic.* New York: The Macmillan Company, 1921.

Moise, Edwin E., and Floyd L. Downs. *Geometry.* Reading, Mass.: Addison-Wesley, 1964, p. 298.

Monroe, W. S. *Development of Arithmetic as a School Subject.* Bulletin No. 10. Washington, D.C.: U.S. Government Printing Office, 1917.

National Council of Teachers of Mathematics. Tenth Yearbook. The Council, 1935.

National Council of Teachers of Mathematics. *The Learning of Mathematics, Its Theory and Practice.* 21st Yearbook. The Council, 1953.

National Cyclopedia of American Biography, XII, 203-4.

National Society for the Study of Education. Part I, 1939, pp. 299-324.

————. 29th Yearbook. Part II, 1930, Chapter 13.

————. *The Scientific Movement in Education.* 37th Yearbook. 1938.

————. 38th Yearbook. Part II, p. 488.

New Thinking in School Mathematics. Report of the Royaumont Seminar. Organization for European Cooperative Development, 1961.

Nimitz, Admiral C. W. "The Importance of Mathematics in the War Effort," *The Mathematics Teacher,* February, 1942, pp. 88-89.

Orleans, Jacob S., and Julia L. Sperling. "Arithmetic Knowledge of Graduate Students," *Journal of Educational Research,* 48:177-86, 1954.

Price, G. "Progress in Mathematics," *Education Digest,* Vol. 27, 6:20-23, February, 1962.

Reisner, E. *The Evolution of the Common School.* New York: The Macmillan Company, 1930.

Rice, Joseph Mayer. *The Public School System of the United States.* New York: The Century Company, 1893.

Russell, Bertrand. *Selected Papers of Bertrand Russell.* Modern Library.

Seaver, E., and G. Walton. *New Franklin Arithmetic,* Second Book. New York: Sheldon & Company, 1895.

Smith, D. E. "Arithmetic" in Paul Monroe, *Cyclopedia of Education,* Vol. I. New York: The Macmillan Company, 1913.

————. *History of Mathematics,* Vols. I and II. New York: Dover, 1923.

————. *The Teaching of Elementary Mathematics.* New York: The Macmillan Company, 1900.

Spitzer, H. F. *The Teaching of Arithmetic.* Cambridge, Mass.: Riverside Press, 1948.

Stern, Catherine. *Children Discover Arithmetic.* New York: Harper and Brothers, 1949.

Stokes, Claude N. *Teaching the Meanings of Arithmetic.* New York: Appleton-Century-Crofts, Inc., 1951, p. 329.

Struik, Dirk J. *A Concise History of Mathematics.* New York: Dover, 1948.

The Reorganization of Secondary School Mathematics. Mathematical Association of America, 1923.

The Report of the Commission on Mathematics. Vol. I. *Program for College Preparatory Mathematics.* Vol. II. *Appendices—Topics in Mathematics.* College Entrance Examination Board, 1959.

Thiele, C. Louis. *Contribution of Generalization to the Learning of the Addition Facts.* Contributions to Education, No. 673. New York: Bureau of Publications, Teachers College, Columbia University, 1938.

Thorndike, Edward L. *The Psychology of Arithmetic.* New York: The Macmillan Company, 1922.

Van Engen, Henry, and Glenadine Gibb. *General Mental Functions Associated with Division.* Educational Service Studies, No. 2. Cedar Falls: Iowa State Teachers College, 1956.

Washburne, C. W. "Mental Age and the Arithmetic Curriculum," *Journal of Educational Psychology,* 23:210-31.

Wheat, H. *How to Teach Arithmetic.* Evanston, Ill.: Row, Peterson & Company, 1951.

Whitehead, A. N., and B. Russell. *Principia Mathematica,* Cambridge, 1912.

Williams, Catherine M. "Arithmetic Learning in an Experience Curriculum," *Educational Research Bulletin,* 28:154-62, 167-68, 1949.

Wilson, G. M. "The Social Utility Theory as Applied to Arithmetic, Its Research Basis, and Some of Its Application," *Journal of Educational Research,* 1948, pp. 321-37.

2

THEORIES OF HOW CHILDREN LEARN MATHEMATICS

Manners with fortunes, humours turn with climes,
Tenets with books, and principles with times.
Alexander Pope, Epistle I, 1733

SURVEY OF LEARNER RESEARCH

The Growth of Experimental Psychology

From the middle of the nineteenth century to the present, consider-able effort has been invested in the search to understand how humans learn.[1] At first, the investigations were almost entirely psychophysical.

---

[1] E. G. Boring, *A History of Experimental Psychology*, 2nd Edition (New York: Appleton-Century-Crofts, Inc., 1950).

In these studies, early researchers hoped to discover laws of human mental processes through the study of physically observable behavior—the speed of response in eyelid flicker, physical growth rates, maximum height and weight attained, digit span, even the physical inclination toward one another of two people sitting in adjacent chairs. This approach was motivated by the supposition that individually different mental functions were related to measurable physical differences. For instance, it seemed likely that reflex speed would be related to rapidity of thought, and hence intelligence. Thus it seemed that study of physical characteristics would provide clues to explain the directly unobservable mental characteristics. But by the end of the century, it was evident that the mind, whatever it was, was much too complex to grasp through investigation restricted to such physical measurements.

During this time, the doctrines of evolution had dramatically influenced the direction of scientific research. The notion that man was different in degree but not in kind from lower animals opened up a new avenue of investigation for psychological research. Instead of attempting to fathom immediately the complex human mental apparatus, it occurred to some that much might be gained by simplifying the problem. Thus, Edward Thorndike, for instance, in his doctoral dissertation under William James, undertook a study of the behavior of chickens.

During the following years many studies on animals ranging from worms to monkeys provided an abundant supply of data concerning the development of memory, emotion, and learned behavior.[2] From these data researchers have been able to formulate hypotheses about human learning based on something more substantial than sheer speculative guessing. From the standpoint of cost-effectiveness, these data provided a basis for selecting hypotheses for further human testing. Those hypotheses actually selected seemed to have the necessary payoff potential to justify the large sums of money and effort required to test their validity.

During the same period in which the study of animal psychology was begun, the direct study of human intelligence underwent its major expansion to date, mainly in the hands of Binet in France and Terman in the United States. From their work came the idea of an intelligence *scale* as well as the measures of Mental Age (MA) and Intelligence

---

[2]See E. L. Thorndike, *Animal Intelligence* (New York: The Macmillan Company, 1898); J. B. Best, "Protopsychology: Behavior in Primitive Worm," *Scientific American*, 208:54-62, February 6, 1963; H. F. Harlow, "The Formation of Learning Sets," *Psychological Review*, 56:51-65, 1949.

Quotient (IQ) which have become so prominent in educational decision making.

But perhaps the most significant trend, at least in the view of many psychologists, has been the effort to develop a deductive methodology, an experimental science of learning. This effort got into full swing by about the 1930's and continues with vigor undiminished today. From it have come many statistical and probabilistic theories of learning, the tools of testing and measurement, and the statistical techniques for analyzing and interpreting the results of test measurements.

Applications of Research in the Classroom

In spite of the effort devoted to the study of learning, it is not possible as yet to describe learning processes in the sort of down-to-earth manner that would seem most practical to the classroom teacher. As a result, the somewhat delicate task exists of motivating the teacher or prospective teacher to study learning research. On the one hand, interest in the results of research quite properly ought to be stimulated but, on the other, one must be careful not to raise false hopes of finding panaceas to instructional problems or produce badly distorted views of the nature and power of psychological research.

To put the matter in perspective, this section reports the nature and results of three illustrative studies. Hopefully, these studies are sufficiently representative of the better work being done in the field to encourage the reader to study other research which is relevant to the teaching and learning of elementary school mathematics.

The Brownell-Moser Study of Meaningful vs. Mechanical Learning[3]

This study is an example of an attempt to utilize the methods of research to shed light on the substance of opposing arguments concerning a methodological question of long standing: Is computational performance improved or hampered by explanations of *why* a process is performed in a certain manner? Obviously, the implications of the study have a direct bearing on instructional theory. If meaningful instruction could be shown to hamper performance, then one could safely proceed to develop skills by precept and practice and save the

---

[3]William A. Brownell and H. E. Moser, *Meaningful versus Mechanical Learning: A Study in Grade III Subtraction,* Duke University Research Studies in Education, No. 8 (Durham, N.C.: Duke University Press, 1949), 207 pp.

valuable time that otherwise would be spent on the needless explanations designed to assure understanding of the skill. On the other hand, if meaningful instruction could be shown to enhance performance, then one could justify the additional time needed to explain the basis of computation.

In the event of the latter outcome, another study would immediately be suggested to determine whether the meaning should be developed prior to exercise, in conjunction with it, or following the attainment of some criterion level of performance. Furthermore, it would then make sense to ask the question how should the meaning be developed; by telling straight out in a clear, logical, efficient manner by the teacher, or by inquiry, exploration, and discovery—a much slower process—on the part of the learner?

In 1942, Brownell and his staff secured the cooperation of several schools to undertake such a study. Experimental groups were established in which third graders were taught to subtract by a particular method, in some cases with meaningful explanations of why the process worked and in other cases without such explanation. Third graders were selected in order to reduce the effects of possible previous knowledge concerning the subtraction algorithms. The investigators made extensive efforts to insure that the experimental groups received the kind of treatment intended. Once satisfied that the treatments had been faithfully carried out, they administered a specially designed test of subtraction performance. The test results supported the case for meaningful instruction and suggested that the best method of teaching subtraction was one called the "decomposition"[4] method.

The study was instrumental in reinforcing the practice of meaningful instruction throughout the grades for *all* processes. It also contributed heavily to the standardization of the decomposition method as the most common method used in this country to teach beginners how to subtract.

Two things about this study are important to note. In spite of a number of practical problems encountered in its execution, enough confidence was generated in its results that many methods-book and textbook authors felt safe in *generalizing* the results. Although the study dealt specifically with one grade level and one operation in one locale, here was evidence on which to base a belief that if other studies were done at other grade levels in other places and with the other

---

[4]See L. J. Brueckner and F. E. Grossnickle, *Making Arithmetic Meaningful* (Philadelphia: The John C. Winston Co., 1953), p. 252 ff. for a description of this and other methods.

processes, similar results in favor of meaningful instruction would be found. To be sure, this study stimulated others to explore these possibilities further. But in the meantime, the important and expensive task of preparing the textbooks which teachers use in a very practical way in the classroom was strongly influenced by the results of this experiment. Experimental research, for all its limitations, had produced a practical payoff.

Secondly, the study raised many questions that required further investigation. Occasionally one finds the attitude that something must be wrong with an experiment that doesn't produce all the answers one might want. But this is the very power of scientific method. In this case, by producing evidence supporting meaningful instruction, the study also implied that further studies into the timing and sequencing of meaningful instruction were potentially worth the effort and expense involved. If the data had not supported meaningful instruction, then subsequent studies would have been directed toward the timing and quantity of drill required to insure skill development. As Suppes reports,[5] relatively little of this latter sort of research has been done until recently, now largely we suspect, due to the impact of the Brownell study.

The Steffe Study of Number Conservation[6]

This study differs from the previous one in that it is less concerned with teaching methodology than with the mental processes associated with developing and maintaining a meaningful concept of number. It grows out of implications of the work of the psychologist, Piaget, who found through a process of extensive interviews evidence of definite "stages" of development in a child's ability to think. On the basis of these studies, Piaget suggested that a child's concept of number at one particular early stage is unstable, being strongly influenced by his immediate perception. For instance, in some clinical interviews with individual children, Piaget found that a child might change his mind about how many pieces of candy were on the table simply as a result of Piaget's rearranging the candy from two somewhat separated groups

---

[5]P. Suppes, *Computer-Assisted Instruction in the Schools: Potentialities, Problems, Prospects,* Technical Report No. 81. Psychology Series (Stanford: Institute for Mathematical Studies in the Sciences, October 29, 1965).

[6]L. P. Steffe, *The Performance of First-Grade Children in Four Levels of Conservation of Numerousness and Three IQ Groups When Solving Arithmetic Addition Problems,* Technical Report No. 14, Research and Development Center for Learning and Re-education, University of Wisconsin, Madison. Center No. C-03, Contract DE5-10-154.

into a single large group, or from a short string in which the candies were placed close together into a long string where they were farther apart. Several kinds of arrangements were used which suggested that children use some intuitive perceptual criterion such as length, density, or mass to estimate even small numbers of things rather than, say, one-to-one matching with the counting numbers.

At a later stage of development, however, Piaget found that the child's concept of number remained unchanged when the physical arrangement of the objects was transformed. So he called this phenomenon "conservation of numerousness."

Steffe set out to investigate conservation of numerousness in a group of American children who had had the benefit of nearly a year of typical arithmetic instruction in the first grade. The practical significance of the study is easy to see. Meaningful instruction of simple addition, at the level of the basic facts, is a common part of first-grade instruction at the present time. Yet, if children cannot conserve numerousness, they can hardly be capable of understanding the meaning of addition. (The basic teaching technique for addition is to have children place, say, 2 objects down in one position and 3 objects in another; then the child forms the union of the two sets by sweeping the objects together in one big pile. If this transformation causes the child to change his mind about how many objects he had before and after the transformation, he certainly would have an incorrect model of what $2 + 3 = 5$ *means*, even though he might be taught to parrot the fact.)

Steffe's data revealed that even after nearly a year of instruction in counting and in the addition of simple numbers, a sizeable number of children did not conserve numerousness. Furthermore, a significant correlation existed between this mental stage and the child's ability—or rather inability—to solve simple arithmetic addition problems.

Thus the results of this study help support Piaget's psychological theory with respect to early arithmetic instruction. Some children in the sample could conserve numerousness while others did not. The results do not suggest what a teacher should *do* to increase the number of pupils who can conserve numerousness or even whether this is a variable subject to instructional influence. Possibly one simply has to await the mental maturation that is slower in coming in some children than in others. Thus, the study raises interesting questions for further research. Is conservation of numerousness modifiable by suitable instructional techniques? If so, what kind of techniques should be used? These questions remain unanswered at the time of this writing.

Nevertheless, practical implications are raised for those teachers who are aware of this phenomenon. The study provides a clue to what the teacher might look for to explain some difficulties beginners may have in learning arithmetic. By rendering otherwise inexplicable behavior understandable, subsequent instruction has a better chance of being adjusted on an individual basis to the reality of the child's limitations.

The Suppes-Groen Study of Counting Models for First Graders[7]

This final example illustrates the effort to find predictive kinds of learning models for particular kinds of content, in this case simple arithmetic counting techniques that first graders might use to solve an addition problem. Because even the most elementary mental problems are surprisingly complicated, this experiment was restricted to the class of addition problems in which the *sum* could not exceed 5. First-graders in their first semester were asked to solve a set of problems of the form

$$m + n = \underline{\hspace{2cm}}$$

where, of course, m and n were specific numbers having a sum less than or equal to 5. Pupil tests were run individually. First the subject was seated in front of a screen resembling a television screen on which the problems appeared one at a time in random order under the control of a computer. In front of him also was a panel with six buttons marked 0, 1, 2, 3, 4, 5. He was to push the correct button to supply the missing sum in each case. Both the answer and the time between presentation of the problem and occurrence of the response (latency) were recorded. After a familiarization period, data for analysis were recorded and stored in the computer operating the system. Although the error rate was nearly zero, the mean latency for the different sums ranged from 2.88 seconds to 5.15 seconds.

One of the objectives of the research was to hypothesize a model of mental process that would enable the researcher to predict the mean latency for each particular problem type: $0 + 0$; $0 + 1$; $1 + 0$; $0 + 2$; $1 + 1$; $2 + 0$; and so on. The study considered five hypothetical counting processes that children might use to find the sums. For each possi-

[7]P. Suppes and G. Groen, "Some Counting Models for First-Grade Performance Data on Simple Addition Facts" in *Research in Mathematics Education*, National Council of Teachers of Mathematics (Washington, D.C.: The Council, 1967), pp. 35-43.

TABLE 1
REGRESSION ESTIMATES FOR THE DIFFERENT SOLUTION TYPES
($\hat{\alpha}$ AND $\hat{\beta}$ MEASURED IN SECONDS)

MODEL	$\hat{\alpha}$	$\hat{\beta}$	s^2
1. x = m + n.	2.96	.216	.569
2. x = n.	3.50	.098	.465
3. x = m.	3.48	.119	.404
4. x = max (m, n).	3.43	.092	.471
5. x = min (m, n).	3.26	.710	.233

TABLE 2

Model 1: x = m + n.

Problem	x	Mean Success Latency (in seconds) Pred.	Obs.
0 + 0	0	2.96	2.98
0 + 1	1	3.18	3.36
1 + 0	1	3.18	3.27
0 + 2	2	3.40	3.57
1 + 1	2	3.40	2.88
2 + 0	2	3.40	3.45
0 + 3	3	3.61	3.48
1 + 2	3	3.61	4.20
2 + 1	3	3.61	4.28
0 + 4	4	3.83	5.48
1 + 3	4	3.83	4.18
2 + 2	4	3.83	3.90
3 + 1	4	3.83	4.04
0 + 5	5	4.05	2.85
1 + 4	5	4.05	4.49
3 + 2	5	4.05	5.15
4 + 1	5	4.05	4.53
5 + 0	5	4.05	5.03

Model 5: x = min (m, n).

Problem	x	Mean Success Latency (in seconds) Pred.	Obs.
0 + 0	0	3.26	2.98
0 + 1	0	3.26	3.36
1 + 0	0	3.26	3.27
0 + 2	0	3.26	3.57
2 + 0	0	3.26	2.88
0 + 3	0	3.26	3.45
0 + 4	0	3.26	3.48
0 + 5	0	3.26	3.40
5 + 0	0	3.26	2.85
1 + 1	1	3.97	5.03
1 + 2	1	3.97	2.67
2 + 1	1	3.97	4.20
1 + 3	1	3.97	4.28
3 + 1	1	3.97	4.18
1 + 4	1	3.97	4.04
2 + 2	2	4.68	4.49
3 + 2	2	4.68	4.55
4 + 1	2	4.68	3.90
5 + 2	2	4.68	5.15

distributed, then this has a t distribution with $n - 2$ degrees of freedom. (In the present case, $n = 19$ [problems], so that $n - 2 = 17$. Although the summation is over subjects, as well as over problems, the details have been omitted so as not to obscure the basic ideas.) While it is not entirely clear whether or not the assumptions of the test are satisfied in the present experiment, its application does provide a rough index of whether or not the fit is satisfactory. The values of $\hat{\alpha}$, $\hat{\beta}$, and s^2 resulting from the analyses of the various models are shown in Table 1. Model 1 and Model 5 provided the best fits (i.e., s^2 was smallest for these models). The second goodness-of-fit computation resulted in levels of significance beyond .05 for all but these models. The predicted success latencies obtained on the basis of Model 1 and Model 5, together with the corresponding observed mean success latencies, are shown in Table 2. Notice that, especially in Model 5, each value of x involves a number of data points. As a result, a clearer notion of the fit can be obtained by comparing the predicted latency with the observed latency averaged over all problems that contribute to a given value of x. This is done in Figure 2. It is clear that the best fit is provided by Model 5. Although there are

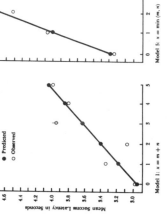

FIGURE 2.—PREDICTED AND OBSERVED MEAN SUCCESS LATENCIES PLOTTED AS A FUNCTION OF x FOR THE TWO BEST-FITTING MODELS

Illustration 6

A page from the Suppes-Groen Study.

ble process, mathematical equations were obtained to predict the latency.

Again the research raised a number of questions that require further investigation. However, even in such a highly theoretical effort as this, some practical suggestions were produced which are relevant to first-grade arithmetic instruction. Of the five counting models hypothesized, the one which gave the best prediction of latency—and therefore might be the best description of the actual process most children use—was *not* the algorithm taught explicitly to the children by their teachers. This result suggests among other things that children do not necessarily learn as they are taught. Thus, by implication, the Brownell study described earlier was a study of instructional method, just as we interpreted it, rather than the study of learning that its title implies. Secondly, in spite of the fact that some discussion of the relation between counting and finding simple sums is common fare in the first grade, no specific algorithm is usually taught for finding these sums as is done later with multi-digit problems. This study therefore suggests one of five possible algorithms as a "best bet" for those teachers who may wish to fill this instructional void.

These three illustrations barely begin to suggest the diversity of experimental research undertaken to improve our understanding of instructional methods, of mental development in children, and of learning. They are included partly to show that careful study can yield practical dividends as well as to indicate the kind of studies that can profitably be carried out. They also reveal something of the trend in research. The last one in particular, with its dependence on the precise measurement of latencies, has been technically feasible only since the advent of the modern electronic computer.

Implications of Psychological Research for Curriculum Development

Yet another area on which psychological research sheds light is of importance to the teacher. In addition to providing specific knowledge of instructional method and learning processes, research has influenced our thinking about several broad questions that are central to curriculum development. Some of these, for instance, relate to (1) the optimum sequencing of topics, either spirally or in self-contained blocks; (2) general approaches to instruction, such as deductive or inductive, directed or autonomous, expository or inquiry oriented, and the like; (3) kinds of content to be included in the curriculum; (4) methods of meeting individual differences effectively; and (5) controlled innovation to yield improved curricula.

We will want to explore such topics in later chapters in some detail. But in order for the reader to see them in perspective, it is helpful first to explore the influence of psychological theory on past practice. Thus, we undertake in the final phase of our historical survey to outline the major ideas of psychological movements which have in some sense become classical, or standard, for various schools of researchers. In each case, the implications of the movement in shaping instruction, our view of the learner, content selection, and sequencing will also be discussed. This discussion will lead us in the next chapter to formulate a systems model of the elementary school mathematics curriculum which takes these important features into account.

Some danger always exists in attempting to summarize a complex field of study. The expert will certainly object that his field has been too narrowly perceived or, conversely, that it has been made to appear excessively comprehensive. The lay person undoubtedly will form some such misimpressions from a quick treatment. Nevertheless, we venture to make a survey not as a substitute for scholarly study but to focus the reader's assumed general familiarity with psychology on problems of arithmetic instruction in the grades. Consequently, some minor distortion of the boundaries between the various schools of thought is tolerable for our purpose. In this spirit, we turn now to the description of the several psychological theories which have had the greatest impact on the elementary school mathematics curriculum.

CLASSICAL THEORIES OF LEARNING

Faculty Psychology

Faculty psychology is one of two mental discipline theories of learning dating back to the Greek tradition (the other being classicism). The mind, in this view, is composed of many distinguishable functions or faculties. The most recent formalization of this theory is known as phrenology and reached a peak of popularity in the nineteenth century. The phrenologists held that the mind was composed of exactly 37 faculties including memory, reasoning, will, and so on. Each faculty was considered to be a sort of mental muscle that required continued exercise for its mature development.

This theory implied that the role of education was to strengthen the desirable faculties through regular exercise and to weaken undesirable faculties by carefully avoiding or suppressing their use. Thus, arithmetic instruction tended toward formal and exceedingly difficult computational exercise in the expectation that the faculty of reason used in this way would become highly developed. In contrast to the modern stress on mathematical ideas, one did not need a deep commitment to the value of mathematics in itself, although its utilitarian value was generally accepted. The real importance of such training for adult life was seen to be the development of the faculty of reason in connection with the process of "transfer." If it were true, as the theory implied, that reasoning was a simple, distinct faculty, then it mattered little what content was involved in its development. Once developed, the faculty would be available for transfer to any situation which required reasoning.

Similarly, memory was considered to be an important faculty which required exercise, and much rote memorization of arithmetic facts and rules was demanded of the child as a result. In the same vein, neatness was a highly valued faculty, one which when properly exercised would transfer to all areas of behavior. Thus, neatness was also strongly stressed in the child's arithmetic work.

It is easy to see how instruction, scope, and sequence were affected by this view of the learner. Instructional method guided by faculty psychology was harsh, taught to the tune of the hickory stick, but nevertheless honestly conceived to be in the best interests of the child. Instruction was expository, the teacher's role being that of task setter and ultimate authority. Individualization of instruction was not a concern. Like modern football players going through their calisthenics, all children were given much the same mathematical exercise. Such teaching was supported by the conviction that if one pupil could do the exercise, in only a matter of time all pupils could do it. After all, reason was considered to be a faculty common to all human beings.

Topics were selected for inclusion in the grade curriculum not because of their intrinsic interest, nor relevance to the present or apparent needs of the child, nor particularly with an eye to the child eventually becoming interested in advanced study of math or science. Rather a suitable topic was one that was difficult, one that could exercise and toughen the appropriate faculty.

Sequence was not based on a concept of child maturation, nor logical order of the content, but rather on a hierarchy of difficulty. Perhaps what one might call the ultimate form of this sequencing was devised and incorporated in the latter part of the nineteenth century. It was called the Grube method. Imported from Germany, the method was basically an inefficient spiral sequence. In the first year, *all four* operations on the numbers from 1 to 10 were taught for mastery. In succeeding years, the range of numbers was extended, finally carried to absurd extremes of difficulty. The great revolt against educational practice of the 1890's, described in the first chapter, found the Grube method a prime target.

Child Psychology

In the late 1800's a new view of the learner began to crystallize, a process in which the theory of evolution served as an important catalyst. Although it may seem strange to the modern mind, childhood is not so much a biological reality as it is a sociological and psychological concept. The concepts of both childhood and adolescence have developed gradually over the last three or four centuries. When Rousseau, in the 1700's, stated that the child is *not* a miniature adult, he was not simply stating a well-known fact but was rather taking fundamental issue with traditional thought. Children *were* viewed as miniature adults and treated as such. If we think, for instance, of the children of the upper classes as they are depicted in the paintings of the era, we see them dressed as diminutive adults. As for the peasant class, children—as miniature adults—shared the burdens of adult labor at a very early age.

It was Rousseau more than any other who began a way of thinking about children that returns again and again to the surface of educational thought and practice. Basically, this view of the child likens him to a growing plant, influenced both by the nurture he receives from his environment and the nature which is predetermined by the constituents of the seed from which he sprang.

This developmental view challenged the faculty model and stimulated a good deal of conjecture concerning the nature of mind, notably that of Locke who proposed that at birth the mind is a blank tablet or *tabula rasa*; of Kant, who saw the mind as the exclusive repository of reality in the form of interpreted sense data, called Idealism; of Herbert Spencer, who viewed the mind as an organism subject to the inexorable laws of evolution and different only in degree rather than kind from that of lower animals; of James, who postulated the creative potential of mind to rise above and indeed modify the natural forces of evolutionary development; and of Johann Herbart, who viewed it as a bank of impressions which required careful storing and continued housekeeping in order to maintain clear connections between knowledge already stored and new information being brought in.

As the concept of childhood gained acceptance, it stimulated the corollary concept of adolescent or the "becoming-adult" stage of life. The first psychologist to thoroughly study the "child" and the "adolescent" was G. Stanley Hall.[8] His work was instrumental in laying the foundation for the Child-Study movement. Several other educational theories find their roots in Hall's work as well, such as the recapitulation theory, mentioned in Chapter 1, and the "wisdom of the body" school popularized by Hall's student, Gesell. Child Study was also instrumental in stimulating the child-testing movement initiated by Binet and Terman.

The impact of child psychology on educational practice in general and the teaching of arithmetic in particular was simply enormous. Certainly it was instrumental in breaking down the formalism and harsh treatment characteristic of nineteenth-century instruction. In so doing, it generated new content selection methods, new sequencing techniques, new roles for teachers, and new kinds of learning experiences.

Two especially important kinds of curriculum thinking grew out of the theory of child psychology. Hall himself was instrumental in bringing Freud to this country in the early 1900's. The impact of Freud's thinking was to focus attention on the ever-present tendency toward abnormal behavior. This focus combined with Dewey's doctrine of the school as a legatee institution to form a strong movement to make the school responsible for the social and psychological adjustment of the child. Arithmetic, in the context of the mentally unhealthy instructional practice of the then recent past, was viewed with suspicion. The intense dislike the study seemed to engender in some children was pointed to as one reason for reducing its role in the curriculum. As a result, formal instruction in arithmetic at the primary level nearly disappeared in many schools in the period from 1930 to 1960. One school of curriculum construction that had much to do with this disappearance stressed the doctrine known as expressionism. The view of the learner fostered by this group was that of a creative artist whom the school would serve best by freeing him to realize his fullest creative potential. This movement represented the very antithesis of authoritarianism. However, efforts to encourage the child toward creativity too often swung to extremes of sentimentalism. As Dewey had to remind his overeager followers in these years, baby does *not* know best (as some of Gesell's adherents interpreted the "wisdom of the body" doctrine to mean).[9] Dewey agreed with humane treatment and the pragmatic selection of topics which were related to the child's needs

---

[8] G. S. Hall. "Child-Study and Its Relation to Education," *The Forum*, 29, 1900.

[9] J. Dewey, *et al.*, *Art and Education*, 2nd Edition (Merion, Pa.: Barnes Foundation Press, 1947), pp. 32-40; J. Dewey, "Progressive Education and the Science of Education," *Progressive Education*, V, 1928, pp. 197-204; J. Dewey, "How Much Freedom in the Schools?" *The New Republic*, LXIII, 1930, pp. 204-6.

and interest. But he urged restraint to curb the sentimentalism that was carried to extremes in the name of democratic process, mental health, and release of the child's creative potential.

The other principal school of curriculum development stressed the doctrine of essentialism. Based on Social Utility Theory, this group urged that only those topics be taught which could be shown to be essential to social needs in the adult world. Although radically different in philosophy from expressionism, both schools of thought had a similar effect on arithmetic in the curriculum: The content was cut to the fundamental processes on some whole numbers and the most common of common fractions. (It is against this kind of curriculum construction that CCSM[10] takes such a strong stand today.) The Social Utility Theorists denied that the schools had a role in social reconstruction and fought with single-minded determination for a practical, efficient, frill-free curriculum.

In sum, child psychology had a profound effect on changing the view of learner from mental muscle to maturing organism. It properly focused attention on the possibility of doing damage to mental development by the application of inappropriate instructional techniques. As a consequence, subject matter was reviewed for inclusion or rejection in the curriculum with the mental hygiene of the learner in mind. The curriculum was greatly diversified as a result. Furthermore, the child was given a role in determining his own education, to explore, inquire, discover, and understand both the intellectual and social universe of which he was a part.

This era was also one of tremendous innovation. It is, in fact, difficult to imagine any educational practice that was not in some way or some place thought of and tried out during the early 1900's. For instance, Pressey did some of the early work on teaching machines; special programs were devised for the slow learner and for the fast learner; administrative techniques were varied to include nongraded team teaching, flexibly scheduled, and a host of other similar experiments; some schools temporarily abandoned the use of evaluative grades in favor of descriptive commentaries of pupil progress; the project method and group activity were developed; and so on. This great splurge of innovation is one reason why teachers today can point to some "new" suggestion and say, quite truthfully, "Why, that was done 'way back when.'" However, the greatest failure of the

---

[10]Cambridge Conference on School Mathematics, *Goals for School Mathematics* (Boston: Houghton Mifflin, 1963), p. 8.

time was the common affliction of educational practice, the tendency to go to extremes. It is a case in point why educational theory must be formulated, understood, and applied in a hardheaded manner not only to stimulate reform but to direct it into profitable channels.

Stimulus-Response Theory

In spite of the development of child psychology, faculty psychology remained the unchallenged guide to instructional practice well past the turn of this century. Already undermined to some extent by the writings of William James, faculty theory was strongly attacked by the research of Thorndike and Woodworth in 1901. The basis of their work was a series of experiments designed to measure the extent to which the transfer of training predicted by faculty theory actually took place. They found that "Training, for instance, in estimating the lengths of short lines resulted in no significant improvement in estimating the lengths of longer lines." Neatness developed in one area of work did not result in neater work in general. Evidence mounted that the faculty psychology was theoretically untenable.[11]

As a result of his studies with animals, the conviction grew in Thorndike that the correct explanation of learning lay in the formation of what he called "bonds," links between particular stimuli (or a certain situation) and the response which resulted from it. He argued that, as a result, there could be no general transfer of learning except to the extent that two situations had identical stimulus elements. Only then might one expect a similarity in the nature of the response. Thus, for instance, Thorndike hypothesized that the stimulus $4 + 2$ is specifically linked to a response, preferably 6. This bond is one that must first be formed, then systematically strengthened through repeated practice, and finally maintained through spaced practice.

In 1920, Thorndike's writing in *The Psychology of Arithmetic*[12] indicated that the role of psychology begins where common sense ends. Its function is to "decide what bonds need to be formed and in what order as means to the most economical attainment of the desired improvement . . ." He illustrates this theory by such examples as "Does the ability to add involve special bonds leading from '27 and 4'

---

[11] E. L. Thorndike and R. S. Woodworth, "The Influence of Improvement in One Mental Function upon the Efficiency of Other Functions," *Psychological Review*, VIII, 1901.

[12] E. L. Thorndike, *The Psychology of Arithmetic* (New York: The Macmillan Company, 1922).

to '31', from '27 and 5' to '32', and '27 and 6' to '33'; or will the bonds leading from '7 and 4' to '11', '7 and 5' to '12' and '7 and 6' to '13' . . . serve as well?"

S-R theory seemed particularly suited to mathematics instruction and in the hands of Thorndike's students, notably Knight, it had a significant impact on the logical sequencing of arithmetic concepts. In Knight's extension of S-R theory, complex learning factors were decomposed first into "unit skills." These units were then ordered in a hierarchical arrangement. The intention was to help the learner to construct more complex bonds from elementary bonds. This scheme became the basis for a number of textbooks written in the 1930's and 1940's.

Thorndike, via his enthusiastic endorsement of the power of science to resolve questions of pedagogy, his remarkably clear experiments, his forceful style, and his S-R theory, made a strong impression on instructional practices also. Much attention was given to the frequency of practice needed to build bonds to just the right strength, depending on whether they had to be broken later or maintained indefinitely. Efficiency was a byword to Thorndike and very much on every educator's mind in that period of rapid expansion of the curriculum. In his view, no overlearning was to be tolerated, only carefully measured and spaced experiences intended to bring about efficient attainment of behavioral objectives.

S-R psychology attempted to create an entirely new view of mind and learning. In the original form of the theory, the existence of mind was simply denied. All that it claimed existed were bonds that connected the input or stimulus to the output or response. The implications for instructional practice were that the bonds, which experiment presumably could discover, would have to be scientifically formed, maintained, and broken at appropriate times and in appropriate ways. The task of science was to spell this process out in detail. However, the plan came essentially to a premature end in the mid-1930's when meaningful theory of instruction became the dominant force in arithmetic teaching.

At first, Thorndike felt that content selection was a matter of values and, therefore, beyond the pale of scientific concern. By the time that he attempted to find ways to include the content selection process in his scientific scheme, it was too late to have a serious impact on common practice. Thus, the main contributions of S-R theory have been in the realm of sequencing, where the notion of hierarchies gained prominence; in instructional practice, where he advocated that concepts be developed inductively and applied deductively; and with regard to a view of mind which was quickly dropped from contention in the arena of classroom practice. As we shall see later, a new behavioral theory has its origins in the old S-R theory and is a very important part of the present educational scene.

Gestalt Psychology

The Gestalt theory of learning, sometimes called Field Theory, was formalized by Max Wertheimer in Germany. Its influence on the arithmetic curriculum became especially evident following the adoption of the meaningful theory of instruction by the NCTM in 1935. According to this theory, learning is neither a process of association of ideas as Herbart believed nor bond formation as Thorndike taught but rather a matter of sensing meaningful patterns in the perceptual fields afforded by one's experience. Patterns are never completely sensed but rather evolve through continued experience. This theory requires a continuous process of relating newly sensed patterns to past understandings. Thus learning is a function of "insight" and maturation. In the Gestalt view, learning is facilitated if the goals are made clear, that is, if the kinds of patterns to be sensed are known, and if the pupil is motivated to seek these perceptions.

Thus by emphasizing the process of discriminating significant patterns which may exist in infinite variety within the perceptual field, Gestalt psychology strongly encourages a methodology which stresses creativity, discovery, and abstraction. Combined with existential philosphy and the notions of being and becoming, Gestalt theory remains a significant influence in education today. Actually, it represents one of two fairly distinct streams identifiable on the present scene, the other being behaviorism. It is difficult to separate the educational effects of this theory from the concurrent effects of the Progressive movement, expressionism, and the Child-Study movement. Gestalt psychology has been highly regarded, and was implemented as the basis for a large number of elementary school arithmetic textbooks in the 1940's and 1950's. But on the whole, this period was a quiescent one in arithmetic instruction. Thus, the contributions of the theory seem somewhat less clearly defined than some of the other movements. Certainly it helped increase emphasis on discovery-oriented teaching and helped sustain the meaningful method of arithmetic instruction. However, it seemed to have less to contribute in the area of content selection and sequencing. Thus both content and sequence remained largely unaffected by this theory.

Neo-behavioral Psychology

In the aftermath of World War II, respect for educational science once more began to rise in conjunction with the growing appreciation of the fruits of science generally. Among the many branches of science and technology which experienced rapid growth in this period was a new area called systems engineering. One specialty within this area was called cybernetics, the study of man-machine systems.[13]

Cybernetics was of special concern to both the military and industry in connection with the trend toward automation. The central problems that cybernetics attempted to solve were (1) to find the optimum role for man and machine in automatic systems and (2) to stabilize the system by a process called "feedback," that is, using a small sample of the output to modify the input in such a way as to keep the output within predetermined limits.

The Air Force was especially active in assigning teams of researchers to the study of cybernetic systems. The knowledge gained in these studies began to be applied to the solution of problems in general learning systems during the 1950's. Many of the Air Force psychologists took positions of importance in the civilian educational structure during these years. Now, the effect of their systems orientation has spread throughout the entire educational establishment.

Perhaps the prime effect has been to revive behaviorism as the basis not only for research but for curriculum construction as well. During the 1950's, the efforts of the previous 30 years to identify curriculum objectives received increasing criticism. The main attack was on their lack of precision. For instance, consider the curriculum objective: "The child should be able to appreciate mathematical thought." The behaviorists asserted that a teacher could never know when or if such an objective had been achieved. The weakness of the objective, in the behavioral view, was that it does not specify the kind of student behavior which defines achievement of the goal.

As a result of this kind of attack, curriculum builders of the behavioral school have achieved considerable success in focusing attention on a search for *behavioral* objectives. These statements are characterized by the use of "action" verbs. Their use enables the teacher to determine through the direct observation of pupil behavior whether or not the goal has been achieved. More will be said about the use of such statements in the chapter on evaluation. By the late 1950's, the philosophy of this movement had gained the ascendancy in

---

[13]N. Wiener, *Cybernetics* (New York: Wiley, 1948); and his *The Human Use of Human Beings* (New York: Houghton Mifflin, 1950).

many teacher training and educational research institutions. As a result, most curriculum construction activities are now behaviorally oriented.

Besides emphasizing behavioral objectives, neo-behaviorism has been influential in promoting programed instruction and the use of teaching machines, and, most importantly, in reawakening interest in building a science of learning through research.[14] This research is being conducted at several centers, probably the largest being the Institute for Mathematical Studies in the Social Sciences at Stanford University. Others especially influential in promoting this kind of objective search for a science of learning include the Research and Development Center for Individualized Instruction at the University of Pittsburgh and the various groups working with the Association for the Advancement of Science on innovative programs in elementary school science.

The psychology which underlies this effort is a much expanded version of Thorndike's S-R Theory. Mainly, it does not exclude, as Thorndike did, the possibility of the mind generating information internally to influence the bond formation. In addition, the theory has been significantly mathematized. This movement accounts for a very large portion of the money and effort now being expended in learning research.

The spirit of this work is clearly related to the kind of investigations one finds in the exact sciences. The motivation for these researchers is the hope that through finding a consistent axiomatic basis for learning, much like Newton found to explain the motion of material bodies, learning too might be brought to a threshold of great progress.

The effects of neo-behaviorism in the classroom have been especially prominent in the last decade. Beginning in the late 1950's, B. F. Skinner of Harvard rejuvenated some learning ideas first put forward by Pressey a quarter century before. Systematizing and adding to these ideas, Skinner developed a teaching machine clearly built on the new systems approach. The learner was viewed as the system operand, a concept not far removed from the notion that Pavlov used in his famous experiment with salivating dogs. The role of instruction was to order the stimuli to which the operand was to be conditioned. A suitable response to the stimulus would be immediately reinforced by some favorable event; inappropriate responses were to be extinguished. This approach has raised questions which are the subject of some debate today. What kind of reinforcement schedules produce optimum rates of learning? What mixture or external reinforcement (by the teacher

---

[14]P. Suppes, "Computer Assisted Instruction in the Schools: Potentialities, Problems, Prospects." Technical Report No. 81, Institute for Mathematical Studies in the Social Sciences, Stanford University, October, 1965, p. 13.

or materials) and internal reinforcement (enjoyment in success by the learner) yields optimum system output?

Some success with the early teaching machines was achieved and by the early 1960's programed materials were widely introduced in the schools. Shortly after, possibly because expectations had been too high, some disillusionment with the usefulness of these devices set in. The effort did not die, but was subdued for a few years. Recently it has been the object of a more conservative and appropriate level of utilization.

The main contribution of programing has been in the area of sequencing a given body of content in order to attain specifically defined behavioral objectives. In the past, minimal importance has been attached to other curricular variables such as teaching method and the use of concrete learning materials. Even individual differences, except for rate of learning, were largely ignored since all learners received essentially the same instructional treatment. The behaviorists are undergoing a curious struggle at this time in regard to the matter of individual differences. On the one hand, such differences are treated as annoying flaws in the human as a research subject. From the experimenters' point of view, such differences simply increase the error of measurement and therefore need to be reduced as much as possible. On the humanistic side, educators have been working very hard to develop the unique capacities of each individual. A philosophical question has not been resolved in terms of the direction the development of learning systems should take: Should individual differences purposely be *increased* by the new instructional methodology *or reduced* as much as possible?

With the rapid growth of computer technology in the last decade, individualized instruction has received an important assist. A variety of experimental work has been done to develop computerized systems capable of sensing and administering to the need for individual treatment. Although certain technological problems and economic considerations have limited the dissemination of computer-assisted instruction, we may expect to see its wider use in the future.

Efforts to develop computer-assisted instruction (CAI) are underway at several centers, among them the Research and Development Center for Individualization of Instruction at the University of Pitts·burgh. Among their many interests is a joint effort between the university and local industry to develop a variety of devices which will facilitate communication between the learner and the computer. This development is one of the important problems that must be solved before learning systems can be most effectively used.

Illustration **7**

Computer-assisted instruction. Photo by RCA.

In sum, neo-behaviorism has had its main thrust at the experimental and research levels to date. Classroom effects have been largely confined so far to the emphasis on establishing behavioral objectives and on the use of programed materials. The potential of the field lies in the area of automated teaching systems. At present, the use of such systems has not been shown to be feasible on a large scale. Exactly what importance they may have in the future is not clear at this time. However, in view of the fact that automated systems seem the best hope at the moment for effective handling of individualized instruction, this area is certain to receive much attention in the coming years.

Piagetian Psychology

At present a distinctly different school of researchers is moving in directions nearly opposite to that of the behaviorists. Among the most prominent names in this stream of activity is that of Jean Piaget. He and his associates have published a remarkable number of books describing their observations of the natural development of the child's concept of number, logic, geometry, the physical world, and a host of others. In all his work, he has identified four stages through which the child progresses as he moves toward maturity. They are the sensory-motor or *preverbal* stage; the *preoperational* stage which extends to about the age of 5 or 6; the *operational* stage which lasts until about age 13; and the *formal* stage which marks the beginning of the mature period.[15] Actually the ages for the corresponding stages may differ widely with individual children. The principal idea is that the fixed *sequence* of stages is common to all children in all areas of mental development.

Since children in elementary school are usually in either the pre-operational or operational stage, these two have been of most interest to teachers. Piaget's theory puts heavy emphasis on the importance of utilizing the child's senses prior to developing his ability to deal with abstractions. Thus, Piaget has been influential in redirecting the movement once again toward the use of concrete objects to develop basic ideas in arithmetic. In general, this trend has resulted in bringing multi-sensory experiences to the child. Good examples of materials developed for this purpose are the well-known Stern Blocks, the Cuisenaire Rods, and the various materials developed more recently by Z. P. Dienes.[16]

The work of J. S. Bruner is related to that of Piaget in some ways and falls well within the confines of the Gestalt theories. His influence on the arithmetic curriculum has been widely recognized, particularly through his emphasis on the use of discovery techniques. He has also been a leader in arguing the need to develop in the child a deep-lying and unified grasp of a field of inquiry through emphasis on its structures. Such instruction, he feels, develops a lively sense of enjoyment in learning. Bruner's pioneering research has also revealed the basic strategies by which humans form concepts or categories of thought.[17] This work has also been instrumental in promoting the use of attribute blocks such as those developed by Vygotsky, Hull, and Dienes.

Among the better known discovery-oriented researchers now working on the important area of teacher education is Robert Davis of Webster College. Although he is somewhat eclectic in the choice of psychological theories which guide his work, his credentials as one

[15] J. H. Flavell, *The Developmental Psychology of Jean Piaget* (Princeton, N.J.: D. Van Nostrand, 1963).

[16] Z. P. Dienes and E. W. Golding, *Learning Logic, Logical Games* (New York: Herder & Herder, 1966).

[17] J. Bruner, J. Goodnow, and G. Austin, *A Study of Thinking* (New York: Wiley, 1956).

Illustration A

Children Employ Manipulative Materials as a Part of the Analysis of Mathematics Instruction Project, under the Direction of Professor Thomas Romberg in the Wisconsin Research and Development Center for Cognitive Learning.

oriented to Field Theory predominate. His work with children emphasizes a low-keyed discovery approach, often in the format of competitive games which require the opposing teams to develop inductively the mathematical abstractions which contain the winning strategy. In some elementary schools, this technique has resulted in remarkable and sustained progress. The fact that it is not universally successful has stimulated a search for the factors which seem to determine the success or nonsuccess of the techniques. Davis discourages the use of external reinforcement schedules, and minimizes the use of written tests to evaluate progress except in certain instances where the pressure on the teacher to "teach for the test" can be confidently known to be neutralized.[18]

---

[18]R. B. Davis, *A Modern Mathematics Program as it Pertains to the Interrelationship of Mathematical Content, Teaching Methods and Classroom Atmosphere* (The Madison Project), Cooperative Research Project No. D-093 (Syracuse University and Webster College, 1965), p. 101.

Further influence of Gestalt psychology can be seen in Davis' concern for the total context in which learning takes place; his interest in the child getting the large context from which he gains novel insights that can be related to earlier experiences; and his use of a large variety of instructional materials to build concrete images of important concepts. He has been most successful in developing the mathematical creativity of children and enhancing the child's interest in and liking for mathematics through the use of these techniques.

Certainly any discussion of notable contributions being developed today under the guidance of field theory must include the work of Z. Dienes. Although most of his work has been done outside the United States, he has recently performed some research with Bruner at Harvard and is now in residence at Quebec, Canada. Perhaps the most striking of his many-faceted experiments are those dealing with teaching set ideas and logic to beginners through the use of "logic blocks." Like Davis, Dienes stresses the use of games to develop ideas inductively, concretely, and very enjoyably from the child's point of view. Dienes' own contributions to learning theory include the identification of three states all of which fall generally within the Piagetian "operational" stage. Dienes' first state is the preliminary *grouping* state "during which situations are handled more or less in the random fashion of a child's playful exploring activity. These activities are eventually directed through the promotion of games which give direction to the activity and 'heighten awareness of the direction in which a new insight is being prepared.'" Dienes' second state is a more structured state in which *rules are recognized* according to which events happen to take place. "This leads to the eventual moment of insight when the whole pattern falls into place." Finally, in his third state the achievement of insight is followed by an almost compulsive desire to *use* the new insight.[19]

Many other important efforts can be cited to illustrate the fact that psychological theory, although incomplete and in many ways in an unsatisfactory state, does have an important effect on both research and classroom instruction. Now the important question is, although theory may help the researcher in important ways, and through research benefit the classroom, can it be of any direct use to a teacher faced with myriad problems often ignored in the carefully controlled experiments of the learning theorist and by the mathematician developing experimental programs?

---

[19] Z. P. Dienes, "On the Learning of Mathematics," *The Arithmetic Teacher*, X (March, 1963), pp. 115-26; *Building Up Mathematics* (revised edition) (London: Hutchinson Educational Ltd., 1965).

How Learning Theory Guides Instructional Decision Making

The Nature and Use of Theory

Of what use is psychological theory to the teachers in the classroom? Some people, especially those who pride themselves on being very practical minded, maintain a feeling of high disdain for theory. One often hears the typical comment, "Well, that sounds all right in theory, but it won't work out in practice," as though there were some necessary antipathy between the two. Let us consider briefly what a theory is and then what one can reasonably expect to gain by the use of theory in practical classroom situations.

The need for theory arises in situations which are too complex to understand, to explain, to predict, or to control without the assistance of some simplifying device. Theory serves as that simplifying device. A good theory is a simplified model of some complex phenomena, a model retaining only the most essential characteristics needed for explanatory or predictive purposes. In this way, unimportant but complicating details are cleared away, so to speak, so that one can see and understand the most essential features of the situation. Sometimes theory and resulting practice do conflict in the sense that theory predicts some result that does not actually occur. In this kind of situation, the model, though generally appropriate to the situation, may be oversimplified. That is, in the process of stripping away the complicating features some essential property has been ignored or possibly has gone unobserved. Thus, resultant theoretical predictions are not in good agreement with observable outcomes.

The Use of Theory to Promote Consistency of Practice

Certainly the classroom is an example of a complex situation. As we have seen, many factors influence the kind of learning that takes place. Now suppose a teacher decides to ignore all theory and to approach his daily tasks in a nontheoretical or empirical manner. In what way would such teaching differ from that guided by theoretical considerations? We might expect first of all that it would lack consistency. If no model of the child—as a child rather than a miniature adult, for example—existed in the teacher's mind, the treatment received by the pupil would vary according to the moods and vicissitudes of the day and hour, sometimes considerate and at other times harsh. For the teacher who is cognizant of the knowledge revealed by the research of child psychologists, treatment of the pupil will be stabilized by a desire to meet the requirements theory indicates are essential to successful learning. So a first plus for theory-guided instruction would be greater consistency or stability in the classroom.

The Use of Theory to Simplify Decision Making

The second advantage theory provides for the teacher is that it reduces the complexity of decision making. Every teacher faces countless moments in working with children which require that some decision be made. For example, when a pupil appears puzzled, should he be told the answer outright, asked a leading question, berated for not paying attention, given more time to think, or what? The complexity accompanying each such situation can be overwhelming. Theory provides consistency through reduction of complexity. If, for instance, the teacher is guided by Gestalt psychology, a consistent effort would be made to provide concrete perceptual fields from which the child has a good chance of discriminating the kinds of patterns which can lead to an integrated concept. If, on the other hand, the teacher is guided by behaviorism, the complex situation which caused the child to be blocked is broken down into very small steps which can be traversed by the child at his own best rate and appropriately reinforced at each step of the way. In any case, the teacher possesses a consistent set of guidelines to help in decision making which results in more efficient and effective learning.

Which theory is best? The answer to this question is not known and probably requires that one ask, best for what purpose? For psychological research and for construction of programed instruction sequences or computer oriented instruction, the behavioral approach has some obvious advantages in that it requires that all essential learning outcomes be specified in such a way that they can be objectively measured. For classroom purposes, this restriction is often excessive. In the view of some authorities, it fails to consider important parts of the learning process, in particular the affective or emotional components of learning. Thus the alternative popular theory at present tends to stress the creative side of learning, the enjoyment that comes from that flash of insight, that "Aha! I've got it!" feeling. The Gestaltists might also criticize the atomization of knowledge into unrelated bits and pieces. This criticism is a little extreme, since no research indicates that programing is less effective in producing integrated concepts than is discovery-based teaching. A good deal depends on the wisdom and knowledge of the teacher, his grasp of the subject matter, his goals, and his understanding of his pupils.

What theory should a classroom teacher adopt? The important thing to realize is that choices are available in the selection of models to guide one's teaching and that the selection should be shaped to the instructional purposes and situation with which one is dealing. This responsibility every professional educator must assume—that he knows his purpose and can select, in accordance with the conditions facing him daily in the classroom, the most appropriate theory for him. If, for instance, one's purpose is to develop a clear and well-remembered set of basic facts or definitions, perhaps the most interesting and probably most efficient way to do this might be through the use of well-written programed material. If, again, one has a class of unusually bright and highly motivated youngsters eager to press out on their own in the search for mathematical knowledge, one might employ the discovery-oriented game approach illustrated by Layman Allen's autoletic games like "Wff'N Proof" or Davis's adaptation of the game of "Go" or Dienes's logic block games.

No one can prescribe a general rule for the teacher to follow. If that could be done, then teaching could be embodied in a mathematical model of some sort and human teachers would be expendable. Precisely because this cannot be done, the teaching profession has little to fear in the way of being displaced by automated instructional systems. And precisely this fact accounts for the burden of professional responsibility one shoulders in accepting a position as teacher. If one is unaware of the important role theory has to play in guiding instruction, or if he is unfamiliar with the essential theoretical features that control the outcome of a learning experience, then he lacks an important qualification for the office of teaching.

FACTORS WHICH INFLUENCE HOW CHILDREN LEARN MATHEMATICS

Teacher-Pupil Relationships

In spite of the many things that we do not know about how children learn mathematics, a few important things are known that enhance a child's understanding of matters mathematical. It is well known, for instance, that children learn better when lessons are enjoyable, when the classroom atmosphere is relaxed, when success is appreciated, and when error is not ridiculed but sympathetically remedied. We know that the best teaching occurs when the interpersonal relations between teacher and pupil are built on a feeling of mutual respect. But these general principles apply equally well to teaching in any subject area. What about mathematics in particular?

Lysophobia

One important idiosyncracy of mathematics and science teaching is noted by Dr. Davis whom we quote here:

A particular difficulty, encountered by virtually every new curriculum Project, has been named "lysophobia" by Professor Robert Karplus, of the Berkeley, California Elementary School Science Curriculum Improvement Study. Whereas science and creative mathematics are essentially and necessarily tentative, uncertain, and open-ended, the traditions of elementary school teaching in many instances are authoritative, definite, absolute, and certain. Schwab, for example, reports (c1964) that he was discouraged by a publisher from reporting that the characteristic number of human chromosome pairs was uncertain. The publisher claimed that teachers would reject a book that failed to give a definite number in answer to such a question . . . [The] difficulty here is with some teachers, not with children. Children know that they live with incompleteness and uncertainty; scientists know that no other state is available to living human beings. Unfortunately, teachers have all too often been taught that every question has exactly one right answer, and that the child is entitled to know what it is—or, perhaps, should even be required to know what it is.[20]

Thus children take naturally to learning mathematics as they naturally learn most other things in life—tentatively, experimentally, creatively. The imposition by the teacher or textbook of fixed forms for all answers, insistence on the *one* correct answer or the *one* correct way of doing a problem or performing an operation can act in opposition to the child's growth. Now all this is not to say that the teacher should swing to the opposite extreme and tolerate all sorts of shoddiness or willful behavior in the name of discovering mathematics. Balance is needed, and probably a first requisite to obtaining this balance is the professional competence that comes from a thorough knowledge of the theory of mathematics, the theory of child development, and the theory of learning.

Rate of Learning

As we have noted previously, children learn the concepts and skills of mathematics at vastly different rates of speed. Exactly what causes this difference is not well known at this time; therefore, it is not always easy to predict which children will take to it rapidly over a long

---

[20]R. B. Davis, *op. cit.*, p. 89.

period of time and which will find the going more difficult. Children with outstanding mathematical talent often display their unusual gifts at an early age, however. It is incumbent upon the teacher to watch for signs of talent and provide the flexibility of instruction that permits it to grow appropriately. At the other extreme, some children have unusual difficulty grasping the ideas and their symbolization. For these children, the teacher must make every effort to provide many more experiences at the concrete level than probably are necessary for the gifted.

Verbalization and Abstraction

In the early years of instruction, children vary considerably in their ability to handle verbalizations and abstract notation. Thus a conservative approach to teaching beginners would allow for the extensive use of concrete models through which mathematical concepts could be attained. Again, the habit of excessive practice would be easy to fall into, either by utilizing the models long after their purpose has been accomplished or dwelling on mathematically nonessential aspects of the models. Concrete materials may be necessary but only clear goals kept in mind by the teacher can make them sufficient to secure effective learning outcomes. It seems most appropriate to develop ideas intuitively at first, using concrete models to aid in the development. Some amount of formalization of the ideas may then be possible. This method is often called the spiral curriculum: a pattern of introducing ideas intuitively, followed by whatever formalization is possible, returning to each set of ideas again and again as the children mature, each time tightening the arguments and concepts in a continual process of improving the group of the concept desired. The spiral curriculum requires systematic and well-articulated instruction over a period of years, conducted by teachers whose plans and purposes are coordinated and shaped toward the same ends. Thus primary teachers should know the long-range mathematical objectives which are to be sought throughout the child's K-12 experiences just as upper-grade teachers should be familiar with the objectives that can feasibly be reached and built upon in the earlier grades.

Independent Inquiry

Among elementary school subjects, mathematics is unique in many ways, one of which is the fact that correctness of work can be determined without requiring recourse to external authority. This fundamental feature of mathematics affecting learning has been largely ignored in past teaching practice. All too often the teacher has insisted on doing as the book says or as he prefers with the consequent impairment of the child's independent ability to establish the appropriateness of his results. In the early years, the child's ability to count can be implemented as the ultimate checking device; later his ability to reach an answer via alternative routes or through the recognition of patterns or by the use of logic can serve to test the correctness of his results. Often the translation of mathematical processes and results into physical examples can be an important checking device. Children *can* learn to think mathematically in this way, but the teacher's authority must be placed in proper perspective.

SUMMARY

We shall have more to say in the following chapters concerning appropriate teaching techniques that are consistent with the way children learn mathematics. We summarize this chapter by encouraging the teacher to acquire the knowledge of theory necessary to the successful execution of instruction and so be equipped to choose from the alternatives available from the present state of knowledge. The theories one accepts, either consciously or subconsciously, determine the nature and quality of the instructional approach in general as well as such particulars as the use of drill, the amount of homework assigned, and so on. Whether classroom practice is an effective reflection of a theory or a shallow participation in a fad depends on the teacher. The highest measure of his professional competence is to be able to demonstrate a knowledgeable and well-balanced use of theory to guide day-to-day classroom practice. Without theory to provide such a guide, instruction will reflect lack of direction, contradictory approaches, and incoherent decisions which result from the inability to cope systematically with the complexity and multiplicity of decisions one faces daily. By providing a simplified model of the learning situation, theory thus has an important effect not only in shaping instruction, but also in deciding the scope and sequence of material presented and in defining the teacher's role in the instructional process.

Topics for Further Investigation

1. Try to find specific illustrations in current arithmetic texts that reflect the influence of:

    (a) Recapitulation theory
    (b) Faculty psychology
    (c) Child Development theory
    (d) Stimulus-Response theory
    (e) Gestalt psychology (Field Theory)
    (f) Neo-behavioral psychology.

2. List some goals of elementary school arithmetic instruction and the theoretical basis that seems best suited to guide the instruction which best accomplishes these goals. This is a speculative exercise but try to establish some sort of rational connection between the means and ends that you choose to discuss.

3. Search the literature relative to computer-assisted instruction to determine the strengths and weaknesses such an approach to instruction has.

4. Investigate the kinds of concrete materials which are available for use in arithmetic instruction today. What objectives do they relate to? How does the use of such materials improve arithmetic instruction?

5. Try to invent a project activity which would be useful in developing a child's mathematical skill or understanding. Alternatively, or possibly in the same connection, you might try to correlate science activities or physical experiments with the development of mathematical concepts.

6. Can you recall specific experiences in which you were taught that there is only one right answer or one correct way of doing a problem? Can you find indications in present textbooks of this same tendency to suppress the search for alternate strategies to accomplish a solution to a problem? Cite instances where possible.

7. Is it always true in arithmetic that one should teach from the particular to the general? From the concrete to the abstract? From the known to the unknown? Create an arithmetic lesson segment that explicitly is based on one or more of these principles. Or try to develop a lesson segment which serves as a counter-example to at least one of these principles.

8. What does the psychologist David Ausubel mean by an "advanced organizer"? See Ausubel's book, *The Psychology of Meaningful Verbal Learning*; is he an advocate of discovery method? What is his position on the relevance of psychological theory to classroom practice?

                                   •

9. Explain the distinction between an external reinforcement schedule and an internal reinforcement schedule. Illustrate a classroom situation in which each might be an appropriate instructional technique for teaching some mathematical idea. Which approach would seem more generally applicable to inquiry-oriented teaching? with CAI?

10. Compare the instructional principles prescribed for arithmetic teachers based on (1) Thorndikean S-R psychology, (2) Social Utility Theory, and (3) Meaningful Theory.[21]

11. Find illustrations of some faculty-exercising problems in a pre-1900 arithmetic textbook. What do you think the real effect of such exercises might have been on the learner?

12. What place would you give to drill in teaching mathematics today? On what psychology do you base your position? Consider qualifying your response according to grade level, type of student, and the like.

13. If research reveals that some mathematical idea or set of ideas *can* be taught at some particular age, does it necessarily follow that this material *should* be incorporated into the curriculum at the corresponding grade level?

14. If you were writing an arithmetic textbook for use in the grades, to which would you give preference in sequencing the material: the logical development of the content or the psychological development (defined by some selected psychology) of the learner?

Bibliography

Ausubel, David P. *The Psychology of Meaningful Verbal Learning*. New York: Grune & Stratton, 1963.

_____. Review of J. S. Bruner's *Toward A Theory of Instruction* in *Harvard Educational Review*, XXXVI (Summer, 1966), pp. 337-40.

_____. "Some Psychological and Educational Limitations of Learning by Discovery," *The Arithmetic Teacher*, Vol. 11, No. 5 (May, 1954), pp. 290-302.

Best, J. B. "Protopsychology: Behavior in Primitive Worm," *Scientific American*, 208:54-62, February 6, 1963.

21Cf. Thorndike's *Psychology of Arithmetic*, 1922; Guy M. Wilson's "The Social Utility Theory as Applied to Arithmetic, Its Research Basis, and Some of Its Applications," *Journal of Educational Research*, January, 1948, pp. 321-37; Brueckner and Grossnickle, *Making Arithmetic Meaningful* (Winston, 1953).

Boring, E. G. *A History of Experimental Psychology*, 2nd Edition. New York: Appleton-Century-Crofts, Inc., 1950.

Briggs, L. J., and D. Angell. "Programed Instruction in Science and Mathematics," Chapter 9 of *Review of Educational Research*, XXXIV, No. 3 (June, 1964), pp. 354-373.

Briggs, L. J., and N. R. Hamilton. "Meaningful Learning and Retention: Practice and Feedback Variables," *Review of Educational Research*, XXXIV, No. 5 (December, 1964), pp. 545-559.

Brownell, W. A. "When Is Arithmetic Meaningful?" *Journal of Educational Research*, 38:481-98, March, 1945.

Brownell, W. A., and H. E. Moser. *Meaningful versus Mechanical Learning: A Study in Grade III Subtraction*. Duke University Research Studies in Education, No. 8. Durham, N.C.: Duke University Press, 1949. 207 pp.

Brueckner, L. J., and F. E. Grossnickle. *Making Arithmetic Meaningful*. Philadelphia: The John C. Winston Co., 1953.

Bruner, J. S. "On Learning Mathematics," *The Mathematics Teacher*, December, 1960.

Bruner, J., J. Goodnow, and G. Austin. *A Study of Thinking*. New York: Wiley, 1956.

Cambridge Conference on School Mathematics. *Goals for School Mathematics*. Boston: Houghton Mifflin, 1963.

Davis, R. B. "Emotion and Thought," *The Mathematics Teacher*, Vol. XLVIII, No. 3 (March, 1955), pp. 133-142.

————. *A Modern Mathematics Program as It Pertains to the Interrelationship of Mathematical Content, Teaching Methods and Classroom Atmosphere*. (The Madison Project) Cooperative Research Project No. D-093. Syracuse University and Webster College, 1965, p. 101.

Dewey, J. "How Much Freedom in the Schools?" *The New Republic*, LXIII, 1930, pp. 204-6.

————. "Progressive Education and the Science of Education," *Progressive Education*, V, 1928, pp. 197-204.

Dewey, J., et al. *Art and Education*, 2nd Edition. Merion, Pa.: Barnes Foundation Press, 1947, pp. 32-40.

Dienes, Z. P. *Building Up Mathematics*, Revised Edition. London: Hutchinson Educational Ltd., 1965.

————. "On the Learning of Mathematics," *The Arithmetic Teacher*, X (March, 1963), pp. 115-26.

————. "Some Basic Processes Involved in Mathematics Learning," *Research in Mathematics Education*. National Council of Teachers of Mathematics, 1967.

Dienes, Z. P., and E. W. Golding. *Learning Logic, Logical Games*. New York: Herder & Herder, 1966.

Dobzhansky, Theodosius. *Mankind Evolving*. Yale University Press, 1962.

Dooley, M. C. "The Relationship between Arithmetic Research and the Content of Arithmetic Textbooks (1900-1957)," *The Arithmetic Teacher,* VII (April, 1960), pp. 178-83.

Flavell, J. H. *The Developmental Psychology of Jean Piaget.* Princeton, N.J.: D. Van Nostrand, 1963.

Friedenberg, Edgar Z. *The Vanishing Adolescent.* Boston: Beacon Press, 1959.

Gagne, R. M. *The Conditions of Learning.* New York: Holt, Rinehart and Winston, 1965.

Hall, G. S. "Child-Study and Its Relation to Education," *The Forum,* 29, 1900.

Harlow, H. F. "The Formation of Learning Sets," *Psychological Review,* 56:51-65, 1949.

Hendrix, G. "Prerequisite to Meaning," *The Mathematics Teacher,* 43:334-39, November, 1950.

Hilton, P. "The Continuing Work of the Cambridge Conference on School Mathematics (CCSM)," *The Arithmetic Teacher,* February, 1966.

Lucow, W. H. "An Experiment with the Cuisenaire Method in Grade Three," *American Educational Research Journal,* Vol. 1, No. 3 (May 1964), pp. 159-167.

Morton, R. L. *Teaching Arithmetic: What Research Says to the Teacher.* Washington, D.C.: Department of Classroom Teachers, NEA, 1953.

Orleans, J. S., and E. Wandt. "The Understanding of Arithmetic Possessed by Teachers," *Elementary School Journal,* 53:501-507, May 1953.

Piaget, Jean. *The Child's Conception of Number.* International Library of Psychology, Philosophy, and Scientific Method. New York: Humanities Press, 1952.

Steffe, L. P. *The Performance of First Grade Children in Four Levels of Conservation of Numerousness and Three IQ Groups When Solving Arithmetic Addition Problems.* Technical Report No. 14, Research and Development Center for Learning and Re-education, University of Wisconsin, Madison: Center No. C-03, Contract OE5-10-154.

Stern, C. *Children Discover Arithmetic.* New York: Harper & Brothers, 1949.

Suppes, P. *Computer-Assisted Instruction in the Schools: Potentialities, Problems, Prospects.* Technical Report No. 81. Psychology Series. Stanford: Institute for Mathematical Studies in the Sciences. October 29, 1965.

Suppes, P., and G. Groen. "Some Counting Models for First-Grade Performance Data on Simple Addition Facts," *Research in Mathematics Education.* National Council of Teachers of Mathematics, Washington, D.C.: The Council, 1967, pp. 35-43.

Suppes, P., M. Jerman, and G. Groen. "Arithmetic Drills and Review on a Computer-Based Teletype," *The Arithmetic Teacher* XIII (April, 1966), 303-09.

Thorndike, E. L. *Animal Intelligence.* New York: The Macmillan Company, 1898.

————. *The Psychology of Arithmetic.* New York: The Macmillan Company, 1922.

Thorndike, E. L., and R. S. Woodworth. "The Influence of Improvement in One Mental Function Upon the Efficiency of Other Functions," *Psychological Review*, VIII, 1901.

Wertheimer, Max. *Productive Thinking*. New York: Harper & Row, 1959.

Wheat, H. G. "Changes and Trends in Arithmetic since 1910," *Improving the Program in Arithmetic* (G. T. Buswell, editor). Pamphlet. Chicago: University of Chicago Press, 1946.

Wiener, N. *Cybernetics*. New York: Wiley, 1948.

————. *The Human Use of Human Beings*. New York: Houghton-Mifflin, 1950.

Wilson, G. M. "The Social Utility Theory as Applied to Arithmetic, Its Research Basis, and Some of Its Applications," *Journal of Educational Research*, January, 1948, pp. 321-37.

Wilson, Guy, *et al. Teaching the New Arithmetic*, 2nd Edition. New York: McGraw-Hill, 1951.

3

A SYSTEMS APPROACH TO THE ELEMENTARY SCHOOL MATHEMATICS CURRICULUM

"Alice laughed: 'There's no use trying,' she said; 'one can't believe impossible things.'
"I daresay you haven't had much practice,' said the Queen. 'When I was younger, I always did it for half an hour a day. Why, sometimes I've believed as many as six impossible things before breakfast.' "
Lewis Carroll, Through the Looking-Glass

The Need for a Systems Model of Curriculum

As we contemplate the lessons that past practice might teach us, it becomes clear that the teacher's main task, the stimulation of productive learning, has often been hampered by a disproportionate emphasis on only one or a few of several basic factors which influence learning outcomes. For instance, in the early days of discipline-oriented instruction, undue emphasis was given to mental gymnastics and computational tricks. The hope was that this emphasis would produce youngsters capable of quick and accurate computation. However,

77

failure to give due consideration to the nature and needs of the learner, to the problems of teacher-pupil interaction, and to the appropriate use of instructional materials often resulted in learning outcomes quite different from those intended.

The developmentalists, reacting to the excesses of formalism, became preoccupied with the child at the expense of content. Social Utility Theorists had their perspectives closed in by a passion for efficiency and practical usefulness. The project-method schools of the Progressivists gave precedence to the child's immediate needs and interests but often failed to provide the sequential development needed for later pursuit in an academic discipline. And so it went, some group in each era stressing one component of good instruction at the expense of others, but all having much the same general effect: inadequate learning of arithmetic.

What of the reform in elementary school mathematics (ESM) that is going on today? The same kind of misplaced emphasis is possible and the same kind of inadequate learning outcome can result. We see a new look in content and methods being urged by the academic specialists, which is appropriate. But the tendency also has been to talk much and do little about such important matters as framing clear and consistent mathematical goals for *today's* schools; of smoothing the way for pupils moving through ESM curricula that are in a state of transition; of deciding and providing the kind and amount of mathematical training needed by teachers; and of finding ways to prepare the child for learning newly advocated mathematical ideas.

If we are really going to damp the excessive vibrations of the educational pendulum and settle down to methods which yield a significant improvement in learning outcomes, proper balance must be given to each of the basic factors on which productive learning depends. The systems approach to curriculum is a means by which this end may be better achieved.

A Systems Model of Curriculum Defined

Curriculum is a term which has meant many things to many people. Among the several authoritative definitions given to it, the ideas of scope and sequence have been undoubtedly the most popular. The tendency in recent years has been to broaden the meaning of the term to include everything associated with learning for which the teacher is responsible. Thus not only is content considered, but also the tactics of instruction, the role of the teacher, and the nature of the learner. By expanding the view of curriculum in this way, we have something more than a word definition. Rather we have a model of all the essential factors which have equally important roles to play in determining the nature of learning outcomes. We have, in other words, the beginning of a systems model of curriculum.

An approach which attempts to take all relevant factors into account in the process of optimizing the performance of a complex system is called a systems approach, a term borrowed from the lexicon of the engineer. In this discussion, the system may be regarded as the curriculum, although "system" is not a fixed notion. A school administrator may see the system as the school; a superintendent, as the school district; and government officials, as the state or national school system.

Two features of the systems approach are particularly helpful in thinking about the performance of something as complex as an educational system. The engineer phrases it in this way: Within the limits set by cost considerations and other system constraints, what set of system parameters yields optimum performance? The two key ideas are embodied in the terms *parameters* and *optimum performance*.

To get a feel for the meaning of *parameter*, imagine a television set that has only a single bright line showing on its face, running diagonally from corner to corner. On the control panel are four knobs labeled *On-Off, Vertical, Horizontal,* and *Brightness*. If the knobs are left untouched, the line stays fixed in a given state. It is either showing or not showing depending upon the "value" of the *off-on* switch; if the line is visible, its horizontal and vertical positions are determined by adjusting the corresponding knobs. Similarly, the brightness is controlled by the value of the brightness knob. These four factors which are adjustable to desired fixed levels are called the system parameters. In other words, parameters are the adjustable characteristics either of a system or of any one of its subsystems which permit one to optimize the performance of the system.

Now consider the problem of adjusting the television system for "optimum" performance. First one must know what *optimum* means. In this simple example, suppose optimum is defined, "the line passes through a point marked on the screen and has maximum visual detectability." With this definition in mind, the systems controller can easily make the necessary adjustments of the parameters to secure optimum performance: off-on control set to *on*; brightness control to *maximum*; vertical and horizontal controls adjusted until the line passes through the desired point. For every system, the definition of optimum performance is obviously an essential prerequisite for its successful operation.

Before leaving this simple analogy to discuss the nature of the ESM system and its parameters, two other concepts need some preliminary explanation. The electrical voltages which are the source of the diagonal line may be termed the system "input." Similarly, the visible line showing on the face of the screen is called the "output." The precise referents of the terms *input* and *output* are determined by the particular system under study. In an ordinary television set, the input is the signal received through space from the transmitting station and the output is the picture you view. The system parameters are channel selector switch, the off-on switch, and the various other controls for brightness, contrast, picture stability, tone control, and so on. In an economic system, the input might be labor, and the output productivity, with fiscal and taxation policies serving as two of many system parameters. Or in an air-defense system, the input might be target radar signals and the output missile control signals.

An essential feature to note concerning any system's behavior is that where several system parameters exist, optimum performance, however defined, is unlikely to be achieved by riveting attention on only one control. Of course, there may be exceptions. If the definition of optimum is greatly simplified, as in our television illustration, for example, by requiring only that the line be visible, then one might achieve optimal learning and secure this optimum performance simply by turning the *off-on* switch to *on*. Similarly in a curriculum system for ESM, one can oversimplify the definition of optimal learning and secure optimum performance by restricting attention to only one or a few of the available parameters. However, in the general case where a sophisticated system is to be tuned up to produce the best possible output of which it is capable, optimum performance will require that the full range of parameters be adjusted skillfully. The questions to be considered now are these: What is a systems model of the ESM curriculum? What are the important inputs to consider, how shall optimum output be defined, and what are the system parameters which need attention and adjustment?

Our review of the historical context of ESM enables us to identify four essential subsystems of the curriculum. We label these (1) mathematics, (2) learners, (3) teachers, and (4) instruction. These subsystems and some of the important parameters associated with each one are identified and schematically related in Figure 3.1.

The *output* of the system is a consequence of the mathematical experiences afforded the child by the curriculum. We call the output "mathematical learning." The total *input*, which shapes the nature of the individual's learning experiences, is partly determined by each of the four subsystems.

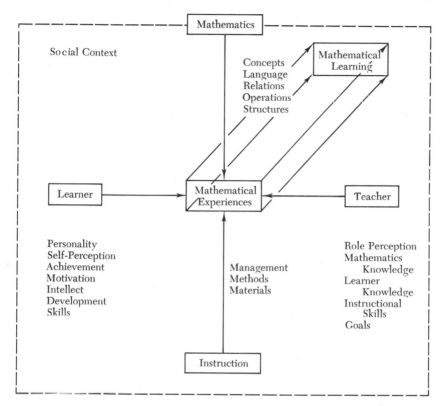

Figure 3.1

A general model for the ESM curriculum.

The dashed line signifies that learning takes place in a social context, an important consideration, but that some aspects of the mathematics content are not primarily a part of the social context. These aspects would be, in a general sense, the intellectual features of mathematics: its abstract concepts, structures, and modes of reasoning.

The usefulness of the model lies in the assistance it gives to organizing our thinking about teaching and learning. Using it in this way, we may consider the effects on learning caused by changing the inputs one at a time or in pairs or in higher order combinations without losing sight of the whole as we focus on one of the parts.

In order to gain familiarity with the model and the method by which we may use it to illustrate a particular curriculum, consider the following examples of some of the historical arithmetic curricula discussed in the previous chapters, this time from a systems point of view.

ILLUSTRATIONS OF SYSTEMS MODELS FOR PAST ARITHMETIC CURRICULA

A Formal-Discipline Model of Curriculum

Recalling the nature of arithmetic education in the pre-1900 period, we might describe the optimized output as that learning which improved both manipulative skills and mental faculties. As evidence of optimal system performance, we should have expected the pupil to exhibit mastery, defined in terms of speed and accuracy, of the four fundamental processes on whole numbers and fractions. Also, his faculties of reason, of good habit, of neatness, and of memory should have been conditioned to the level required for the performance of whatever duties he may have been assigned in his adult station in life.

This view of life and education established arithmetic content as an important input to the system. The main content parameters were the kinds of number ideas taught, the types of processes, the level of difficulty, and the kind and amount of mathematical symbolization employed.

The view of the learner as a subsystem within the curriculum is especially critical. One imagines a sort of ideal child, not in the sense of being perfect but as being somewhat less complicated than an adult. The learner parameters that can be influenced either by the teacher, general life experiences, or natural growth have to do in general with his intellect, his emotions, and his will. In the discipline model, the teacher's authority was applied to make the will of the child conform to the rules of the system. The learner parameters which have a strong affect on controlling emotions were too little understood to be affected by anything other than mere chance or sheer force, and the intellectual parameters were considered mainly as certain habits of performance that needed to be developed. Thus all pupils were expected to listen quietly to explanations, exhibit disciplined behavior, follow instructions, aspire to error-free performance of the fundamental processes, show quick recollection of important facts, and prepare assignments on time with due regard for neatness and accuracy.

The teacher, like the learner, is considered as an idealized and very much simplified subsystem in the total curriculum model. The characteristics or parameters of the teacher input that must be adjusted depend on the particular model. In the one now under discussion, the teacher was viewed mainly as a taskmaster. Therefore, he defined the purpose and procedure for tasks which the pupils were to perform, he maintained a quiet room to insure clear communication and undisturbed practice, he corrected and graded the work in accordance with high standards of neatness and accuracy, and he periodically tested the pupils on memorized facts and rules as well as speed of computation. He needed to know no mathematics beyond the very processes he might be expected to direct the children to perform, he needed to have a firm hand in controlling the pupils, and he needed to be a good drillmaster.

The instructional input parameters fall into three basic groups: classroom management policies, instructional methods employed, and kinds of materials used. Of necessity, as we have seen, classroom management was forced by high pupil-teacher ratios to be inflexible. Thus individual differences among the pupils were largely ignored. Although the pupils were all given a common treatment, they were expected to learn from their mistakes. The dunce cap and hickory stick were primitive attempts at maintaining this internal "feedback" in the system. In general, *feedback* is a systems concept which refers to the use of output performance characteristics to modify some part of the input. For instance, if many errors occur in the output, these errors are analyzed so that the instructional input can be modified in such a way as to reduce the error rate. In the older systems, feedback was left by default to the pupil. As a consequence, systems failure could often be traced to a failure in this internal feedback link. Instructional methods were variable but tended to follow a prescription of rule, example, and drill. The content sequence was controlled by the teacher or textbook according to presumed order of difficulty. The use of concrete materials varied from time to time and place to place. In the middle 1800's and again in the early 1900's, the use of certain concrete materials was strongly advocated, especially for the first stages of arithmetic instruction.

Instruction was mainly expository, showing first by clear example how a process was to be performed. This exposition was followed by the presentation of a performance rule which was to be memorized by the pupil, after which the drill exercises were assigned. The exact form for the answers as well as the desired form for the arrangement of the work on the page were given by the teacher or text. To insure maximum neatness, children were encouraged to do scratchwork separately and record only the answers for the teacher to see and correct.

It is interesting to see how this model has evolved over time into succeeding forms of arithmetic systems, some controls being "tuned up" in the process of change, others falling into disuse, and new ones being built into the new systems. Our next example is both a consequence and a reaction to the unsatisfactory output of the model just discussed. We shall call this next system the stimulus-response model of arithmetic curriculum.

A Stimulus-Response Model of Curriculum

The definition of optimal output for the S-R model can be summed up in the words of Edward Thorndike as found on the first page of his *Psychology of Arithmetic*.[1] The child must *learn* the *meaning of numbers*, the *basic operations*, and *decimal numeration*. Evidence of optimal system output will be shown by the child when he achieves mastery of the fundamental operations on whole numbers, fractions, and measured quantities and when he displays an ability to solve problems of common occurrence in business life. In a set of four amendments, Thorndike reveals how the new definition of what we are calling optimum system output differs from that of the discipline model. First of all, the semantics of mathematical language are to be stressed so that the child will know, for example, that 354 *means* 300 + 50 + 4. Furthermore, empty formalism and unrelated-to-life problem solving is to be replaced by an ability to solve the "quantitative problems of life." Thus we see that the S-R model defines an optimum learning output that differs in two important ways from that of the discipline model: first, in stressing semantic meaning of the common arithmetic symbols and, second, in stressing real-life problems in place of purely gymnastic exercises.

The S-R view of the child input to the curriculum also differs in a fundamental way from that of the discipline model. In the faculty theory, the child is treated as a sort of mental muscle which needs conditioning; the S-R theory denies the existence of "mind" altogether and sees in the learner only a bundle of "original tendencies." It is the task of instruction to utilize these tendencies to construct links or bonds between certain kinds of stimuli or situations and specific kinds of

---

[1]E. L. Thorndike, *The Psychology of Arithmetic* (New York: The Macmillan Company, 1922).

responses. Since children were seen to differ from one another in the kinds of bonds that their minds could construct, in their natural inclination to form bonds, in their interest, and in their motivation, the S-R theory demanded more of the curriculum in the way of individualized instruction.

These changes in the model necessitated a change in the idealized teacher input. The taskmaster parameter was tuned down, so to speak, and other teacher functions were emphasized instead. In the S-R model the teacher's main role was that of organizer and sequencer of material, a role which required constant monitoring of the pupil's behavior to determine the short-term sequencing. Thus the teacher played the main role of feedback link, rather than the child as in the previous model. The teacher monitored the different responses of the children and redirected the formation of bonds accordingly.

The content input was changed largely because of the ascendancy of the doctrine of social utility. Thorndike cautioned that "Bonds should not be formed between articles of commerce and grossly inaccurate prices therefore, between events and grossly improbable consequences, . . . nor between things, qualities, and events which have no important connections one with another in the real world."[2] But rather, bonds were to be formed in the context of practical, true-to-life situations.

In terms of instructional input, the teacher was to show by example "how to do it," then present the rule for doing it, and finally prescribe the drill necessary to form the required bonds. Thorndike called this the inductive method because one went from particular examples to general rules. And although he insisted that children understand the meaning of numerals, as we indicated earlier, he was strongly opposed to elaborating the meaning of computational algorithms except possibly for the brightest and best of the children. The instructional settings placed great demands upon the teacher to watch carefully so that neither underlearning (too weak bonds) nor overlearning (time wasted on bonds already firmly established) would occur. Furthermore, if at all possible, only such bonds were to be formed that would not have to be broken at a later time.

For a variety of reasons, the S-R model failed to produce optimal arithmetic learning as its output. The main successor to this model was the one we shall next describe, one labeled the meaningful model of curriculum.

---

[2]*Ibid.*, 91.

LONG DIVISION : DEDUCTIVE EXPLANATION

To Divide by Long Division

1. Let it be required to divide 34531 by 15.

Operation

Dividend

Divisor 15)34531(2302$\frac{1}{15}$ Quotient

    30
    ——
    45
    45
    ——
     31
     30
     ——
      1   Remainder

For convenience we write the divisor at the left and the quotient at the right of the dividend, and begin to divide as in Short Division.

15 is contained in 3 ten-thousands 0 ten-thousands times; therefore, there will be 0 ten-thousands in the quotient. Take 34 thousands; 15 is contained in 34 thousands 2 thousands times; we write the 2 thousands in the quotient. 15×2 thousands = 30 thousands, which, subtracted from 34 thousands, leaves 4 thousands = 40 hundreds. Adding the 5 hundreds, we have 45 hundreds.

15 in 45 hundreds 3 hundreds times; we write the 3 hundreds in the quotient. 15×3 hundreds = 45 hundreds, which subtracted from 45 hundreds, leaves nothing. Adding the 3 tens, we have 3 tens.

15 in 3 tens 0 tens times; we write 0 tens in the quotient. Adding to the three tens, which equal 30 units, the 1 unit, we have 31 units.

15 in 31 units 2 units times; we write the 2 units in the quotient. 15×2 units = 30 units, which, subtracted from 31 units, leaves 1 unit as a remainder. Indicating the division of the 1 unit, we annex the fractional expression, $\frac{1}{15}$ unit, to the integral part of the quotient.

Therefore, 34531 divided by 15 is equal to 2302$\frac{1}{15}$.

[B. Greenleaf, *Practical Arithmetic*, '73, p. 49.]

Illustration 8

Pages from Thorndike's Psychology of Arithmetic.

A "Meaningful" Model of Curriculum

As mathematicians use certain words such as "real" numbers which are, of course, no more real than "rational" numbers are reasonable, curriculum builders have employed words as simple labels to emphasize some strongly felt position at some time in history. The meaningful model was not, indeed is not, especially meaningful except in a very narrow sense. But it can be characterized in a manner similar to the preceding models, by the nature of its input parameters and its definition of optimal output. We will examine the subtleties involved in the changing meaning of meaningfulness more fully in the next chapter.

The definition of optimal output for this model of the arithmetic curriculum is summed up in the Gestalt concept of *insight*. Above all, learning was to result in insight into the rationale and social utility of the various arithmetic processes. Evidence of success would be a learner who was *well-rounded, intelligent in quantitative situations, creative, resourceful,* and *ingenious* in the use of numbers.[3]

The mathematics content parameters are identical with those given for the S-R model. Emphasis remained on the utilitarian selection of concepts and processes.[4]

However, the instructional parameters were sharply altered from the settings of the S-R model. Superimposed on what was considered a discovery approach to the subject matter units was an elaborate structure of activities called experience units. Through the experience units the insight, the vitality, the interest, and the motivation of the learner were to be activated. One gets the flavor of what was expected from the experience units by examining the descriptive terms that have become enshrined in the basic principles taught in most beginning Math Ed courses. Instruction was to include *rich* experience dealing with *broad* areas; make *present* experience *vivid* and *meaningful*; include a *wide variety* of *meaningful experiences*; provide *flexible work periods*; be adapted to the *needs, interests,* and *abilities*; emphasize *intrinsic motives*: *needs, wants, desires*; develop *relationships* systematically; *direct growth* from immature to mature levels, and so on.[5] Primarily through the experience units, meaningful insight into the social value of what was otherwise conceived to be dull and dry arithmetic content would occur.

The teacher input was also markedly different from that of the previous two models. The authoritarian content-organizer, content-sequencer parameters were de-emphasized and in their place new roles were given precedence. The teacher was first of all to be a democratic leader, then a facilitator, a helpful guide, a person who could assist the pupils in the planning and selection of the wide variety of

[3]L. J. Brueckner and F. E. Grossnickle, *Making Arithmetic Meaningful* (Philadelphia: The John C. Winston Co., 1953), pp. 22-23.

[4]*Ibid.*, p. 58.

[5]*Ibid.*, p. 22.

activities for the day, an organizer primarily of children and learning materials rather than of content, and finally a flexible manager of time and materials to meet individual needs. Subject matter instruction was to begin with many examples, to provide a perceptual field in which the child would finally discover through that sudden flash of insight some arithmetically important pattern. The wide variety of social activities, projects, and so forth would then make this pattern meaningful when the child saw how it could be put to use in real life settings. Thus the model was claimed to be democratic, meaningful, insightful, discovery-oriented, and child-centered.

The view of the learner was basically Rousseauian: developing, maturing, and in need of experiences both meaningful and relevant to his immediate stage of development.

Critique of the Three Curriculum Models

Several points need to be made concerning what we may call the three "classical" models of the arithmetic curriculum before proceeding to a characterization of some currently projected models for ESM in tomorrow's schools. First, the matter of interaction between the components of the system is important. Consider, for instance, how one's view of the learner drastically affects both the other system inputs and the output. At the one extreme are the disciplinarians who see the learner mainly as mental muscle and therefore attempt to condition him by rule and rote; the other are the sentimentalistic neo-Rousseauians who hold no project, field trip, or real-life problem situation too time consuming to nurture the "growing plant" with a broad understanding of the important social applications of number.

Thus, it is important to note that a first requisite for good curriculum planning is to define the essential parameters of not just one or another input, but of every one that is important to the system performance. In spite of the so-called child-centered curricula of the past, one input often neglected in thinking about ESM curricula is one's view of man. Another, as we shall develop more fully in succeeding chapters, is the content input. Altogether too much attention has been centered on the seemingly *practical* aspects of instruction such as textbook selection, classroom management and discipline, and concrete learning aids. While these considerations are or can be important, the particular decisions one makes in regard to them can be greatly affected by both the definition one accepts for optimal learning and the other input parameter adjustments that are made in the system.

This brings us to the second point, the obviously unanticipated outcomes that result from inattention to or inadequately defined input parameters. None of the curricula described so far really came very close to its defined optimum performance. As we have reported earlier, a wealth of information attests to the inadequacy of each of these systems in achieving its desired outcomes. Discipline-trained children for the most part developed a strong dislike for arithmetic and showed poor skill on the average. Thorndike's attempt at a scientific solution resulted in no better arithmetic learning productivity. Finally, meaningful theory became so distracted by time-consuming social activities that the children gained little insight, understanding, or competence in the skills and problem-solving power of arithmetic.

The final point to be noted in connection with this review of classical arithmetic curriculum systems is related to the functioning of the feedback loop. Feedback is the control element necessary to stabilize the system. It provides the means of making the essential moment-by-moment compensations needed to adjust for optimum output. Only two choices for the feedback link in these systems have been possible: the pupil and the teacher. This fact is important because we are going to see in one of the following examples how advancing technology is providing an important third possibility, a kind of automated link that can serve in quite a new and vital capacity.

Of course, both the pupil and the teacher must function in feedback roles in any curriculum system. In some systems, a more critical role falls to one more than to the other. In discipline systems, the child is held primarily responsible for learning from his mistakes and correcting them. For those children capable of doing this, a nearly optimum output for the system can be achieved. For the many children who for various reasons are unable to do this, the feedback loop fails, the system goes out of control, and a systems failure occurs.

On the other hand, systems which make the teacher the critical link for feedback make heavy demands on the knowledge and capabilities of the individual teacher in order to keep the system productive. To the extent that the individual teacher has the necessary wellsprings of energy, dedication, resourcefulness, knowledge, and personality, the feedback exists and the system output is optimized. But the demands on the teacher are enormous, as every experienced teacher knows. And since teachers are as individually different as their students, it is simply impossible for all to function with equal effectiveness as the feedback element of the system. The sheer strain of attempting to monitor all the individual outputs coming from many learners, retaining the mass of information over a period of weeks or even semesters, and then adjusting the various inputs to achieve optimum performance is clearly beyond the limits of ordinary human ability.

For this reason, systems have been necessarily simplified. Individual needs of children have not been well met because it has been beyond the technical capability of our curricula in the past to meet them. Broad mathematical goals have been restricted to those of narrow utilitarian value as a necessary consequence of the technical limitations of our systems. Neither the teachers nor the curriculum builders of the past have lacked imagination, foresight, inventiveness, dedication, industry, or vision. But deficiencies have been severe in the technical capacity of our learning systems to achieve the optimal output. Thus the failures have been primarily systems failures.

One important implication of these failures is, as we shall see in a later chapter, that evaluation procedures must be broadened beyond the traditional, limited evaluation of the pupil to include comprehensive evaluation of all the relevant inputs which contribute to the success or failure of the total ESM curriculum system.

As a result of systems failures in past curricula, we are involved in another attempt to reform the curriculum in mathematics at both the elementary school level and other levels. The important question is, shall we do better than our predecessors or shall we simply introduce another disturbance in the flow of affairs that will only serve as the stimulus for another reaction some time in the future?

Much of the curriculum building needed to effect any educational reform must be done at the local level by virtue of the nature of our educational system. Hopefully, the teachers of ESM will take an important hand in this work in the future. But in order to avoid something like the sight of the golfer who appeared on the links one morning equipped with snowshoes, football pads, scuba mask, and baseball bat to drive the agate sitting on the tee, the essential components of the system must be appropriately shaped to the kind of system performance desired. Even if all the system components are properly taken into account, the output will still depend to a large extent on the skill and art of individual teachers who put the system into operation. But at least the possibility of some reasonable approximation to optimum output will be insured. Failure to consider some of the components, or the assumption of a doctrinaire stance directed toward the past could easily have the same affect on output as failing to turn the switch "on" in our previous television-simulated system: a "no-go" systems failure.

In order to get an idea of the features that are likely to be stressed in some future ESM system, we turn to the description of two models that are among the most modern of modern mathematics reform proposals. The first of these models is patterned after the recommendations of the Cambridge Conference on School Mathematics.[6] It is not intended to be a practical model in the sense of being ready for implementation in the classroom. However, it serves to point up clearly the distinction between traditional and future definitions of optimal ESM learning.

The second model is one patterned after the work of Professor R. B. Davis and the Madison Project. This ESM model is also in an experimental stage although attempts are being made to implement some of its features on a broad scale at the present time. One of its most interesting features, and the main reason for including it in this discussion, is that it is an example of a dynamic curriculum model in contrast to the static nature of those previously discussed.

The reader should note that the following curriculum models are *not* transcriptions of officially formulated statements by any curriculum development group. Rather they are the authors' interpretations of the spirit of important movements in the field of ESM curriculum development at the present time. To our knowledge, no previous attempt to formulate systems models for these specific curricula has been made.

PROJECTED SYSTEMS MODELS FOR ESM CURRICULA

A "CCSM" Model of Curriculum[7]

We define the optimum output of this system in terms of the ideal educated man living in an advanced industrial society. This means, first of all, that the mathematical learning experience must have a powerful humanizing effect on the learner. Thus, in particular, the learner should "become acquainted with the works of genius."[8] Moreover, he should come to realize the wellsprings of mathematical ability that lie within himself. This realization will be evidenced by a sense of confidence in his own analytical abilities, a sense of independence from rather than abject reliance on memorized rules and formulas. In a broader sense still, the learner will understand what mathematics is

---

[6]Cambridge Conference on School Mathematics, *Goals for School Mathematics* (Boston: Houghton-Mifflin, 1963).

[7]CCSM, *op. cit.*

[8]*Ibid.*, p. 9.

and what it is not; and what problems it can suitably be applied to and those which it cannot. By learning the precise language of mathematics and its peculiar modes of analysis, the learner will be a clearer and more logical thinker. Last and intellectually least, but nevertheless important, he will be able to demonstrate abilities above present levels of proficiency in arithmetic computation and in fluency of manipulation of mathematical symbols in general.

What parameters of the learner input must be considered to insure the system's successful operation? In this model, the learner is regarded as a latent intellectual, a quality which CCSM participants felt has been too often overlooked in the past: "We believe that arithmetic as it has been taught in grade schools until quite recently has such a meagre intellectual content that the oft-noted reaction against the subject is not an unfortunate rebellion against a difficult subject, but a perfectly proper response to a preoccupation with triviality."[9] The learner is seen as a creative individual, capable of independent thinking.[10] He has *innate* interest in working at creative problems, and is responsive to the urgings of a *competitive* nature to apply himself to their solution. However, he can be injured by embarrassment and subdued by authority, both effects contributing heavily to systems failure.

What is the nature of the teacher input to this system? The first requirement is that the teacher be mathematically literate, possessing relative to past standards a "deeper mastery, in a purely mathematical sense, of the subject matter."[11] This essential requirement *enables* him to direct effectively the process of inquiry, that he be able to "recognize, as quickly as possible, the validity of unexpected responses."[12] The teacher must be able to see, beyond superficial error in a response, the possible existence of important ideas and be able to direct the inquiry toward the discovery of that knowledge. The level of the teacher's knowledge must be such that he will be "pleased, rather than embarrassed by nearly all the questions that an eager and able student is likely to ask."[13] Failure in this input to the curriculum may lead to results which "may easily be worse than the results that we are getting now."[14] Thus the view of the teacher is the Socratic view of a deep,

---

[9]*Ibid.*, p. 8.
[10]*Ibid.*, p. 17.
[11]*Ibid.*, p. 26.
[12]*Ibid.*, p. 26.
[13]*Ibid.*, p. 27.
[14]*Ibid.*, p. 27.

knowledgeable person, able to establish the kind of intimate rapport necessary to lead successful inquiry, and one sensitive to the needs and nature of the learner who is making the inquiry. This input differs sharply from the emphasis placed on the taskmaster, drill master, facilitator, sequencer, organizer parameters of previously discussed teacher roles. Many of these technician's skills are encompassed in this present view. But the requirement that places the main demand on the teacher is that he have a professional's appreciation of that content of mathematics, the real number system and geometry, which is ultimately the knowledge which he must guide his pupils to know and value.

The instructional input is thus determined by the other components of the system. From the conviction that "the present apparent limits on the insight and creativity of children are being set by the materials presented to them, and not by the native talent of the children,"[15] it follows that instruction must break these constraints and lead by a combination of discovery methods and knowledgeable exposition to the learning experiences which will yield optimum output. To aid discovery, "the teacher should be prepared to introduce required ideas when they are not forthcoming from the class; . . . he should bring attention to misleading statements in the way of the discussion, and summarize results clearly as they come forward. He should not allow the 'moments of triumph' to pass unnoticed."[16]

In the early years, a teacher-aided discovery approach should predominate. But by the intermediate years, a transition should take place toward creative thinking and independent work by the student in learning many of the concepts and proofs of theorems. At this stage, more emphasis should be placed on classroom exercise and homework. Skills should be developed by utilizing them in the development of new work and new ideas. Drill for drill's sake is to be abandoned. ". . . the means of imparting [technical] skill need not rest on methodical drill. We believe that entirely adequate technical practice can be woven into the acquisition of new concepts. But our belief goes farther. It is not merely that adequate practice *can* be given along with more mathematics; we believe that this is the only truly effective way to impart technical skills. Pages of drill sums and repetitious 'real-life' problems have less than no merit; they impede the learning process."[17] Accuracy is considered more important than speed[18] and

---

[15]*Ibid.*, p. 26.
[16]*Ibid.*, p. 17.
[17]*Ibid.*, p. 8.
[18]*Ibid.*, p. 16.

therefore "adequate time for checking should be allowed and methods of checking discussed." The child should especially be rewarded for knowing how to go back to fundamentals, even if the resulting algorithm developed is operationally clumsy. Nevertheless, more powerful algorithms should be learned ultimately. Attempts to individualize instruction will have to be made, for "the intercalation of enrichment material to attract the attention of the more gifted student may no longer suffice to keep children of the same age together, in which case it will become totally impractical to teach mathematics on a grade basis."[19]

The content input to the system falls mainly into two categories, (1) the real number system, and (2) the basic ideas of synthetic and analytic geometry. A true familiarity with both by the learner is regarded as an essential output of the system. Concepts are selected for inclusion in the curriculum not because they are modern but "because they are useful in organizing the material we want to present."[20] The language, notation, and symbolism used should not obscure the mathematical ideas. Since, in mathematics, the function of language "is to communicate with extraordinary precision . . . special terms are good or bad exactly according to their effectiveness in communication, and the same applies to special notations and symbols."[21] In order to improve the "appallingly sloppy"[22] logic of everyday life, the "general use of good logic by teachers will pay dividends in terms of the logic subsequently used by the children."[23] With regard to problem solving, the first emphasis should be on understanding the mathematical structure of the problem and secondarily on getting the "answer."[24]

A 'Madison Project' Model of Curriculum

Whereas the previous model is regarded as an attempt to outline in sharp relief the long-range ideal for ESM curriculum planners, this next example illustrates one practical and creative approach to the implementation of similar ideals within the present constraints on curriculum development. Also, it is an example of an attempt to create a dynamic curriculum; that is, one which has built into it the

---

[19]*Ibid.*
[20]*Ibid.*, p. 10.
[21]*Ibid.*
[22]*Ibid.*, p. 34.
[23]*Ibid.*
[24]*Ibid.*, p. 36.

mechanism to adapt continuously to the ever-changing needs of the time.[25]

The optimal output for this system is a child having the following cognitive and affective attributes: (1) He should be capable of independent exploration behavior in mathematics and be able to "discover patterns in abstract situations." (2) He should have "an appropriate set of mental symbols that represent mathematical situations in a pseudo-geometric, pseudo-isomorphic fashion" and be functionally familiar with fundamental concepts, "such as *variable, function, graph, matrix, isomorphism,* etc." (3) He should exhibit mastery of fundamental techniques and know basic facts. (4) He should view mathematics as discoverable and be confident of his own ability to make such discoveries himself; thus he should believe that mathematics is an open-ended field of inquiry. (5) He should value rational analytical thinking as well as educated intuition. (6) He should "regard mathematics as 'fun' or 'exciting' or 'challenging' or 'rewarding' or 'worthwhile' " and (7) possess an historical perspective of the "heritage of accumulated culture, particularly as the history of ideas involves mathematics, in relation to broad historical perspectives, from prehistoric times until the present." (8) He should feel comfortable in using mathematics in the solution of physical or social problems, as it is applicable.

The nature of the cognitive portion of the output determines the selection of content. The content may be grouped in categories of basic arithmetic, geometry, algebra, logic, and measurement-statistics. The basic arithmetic includes the concept of number and process of counting; the concepts of the four fundamental operations; place-value numeration; the number line; the arithmetic of signed numbers (integers); and the arithmetic of rational numbers. Geometry is primarily oriented toward the analytic side: Cartesian coordinates and graphing; the main synthetic concepts include angle, area, and volume. Algebra content centers on ideas of function, variables, open sentences, identities, simultaneous equations, conic sections, and certain trigonometric, exponential, and polynomial functions. A decidedly new element of content at the ESM level is the algebra of matrices. Logic concepts include implication, contradiction, uniqueness, axioms and theorems, derivations or proofs, and inductive and deductive modes of proof. Applications of mathematics to the real world involve a number of

[25]R. B. Davis, *A Modern Mathematics Program as It Pertains to the Interrelationship of Mathematical Content, Teaching Methods, and Classroom Atmosphere* (The Madison Project), Cooperative Research Project No. D-093 (Syracuse University and Webster College, 1965).

elementary science investigations which require measuring to be done. From this investigation, the process of measurement, measurement error concept, and certain statistical notions such as average and variance are emphasized.

The Madison Project's view of the learner is in harmony with that of the CCSM on most points. A general feeling as a result of the Madison Project work to date is that the intellectual springs of children have not been tapped in any significant way by the traditional arithmetic curriculum. Whether they be the culturally deprived, slow learners, normal children, or exceptionally talented, the Project shows a firm belief in the potential of children in grades 2-9 to learn significant portions of mathematics formerly reserved for high school and college. Not all learn the same amount or to the same degree, but intellectual enrichment of the ESM curriculum is regarded as a must in view of the intellectual capacities found in most children of elementary school age. Thus the view of the learner input is essentially the same as that described in the previous model.

The teacher input is also viewed much like that described in the CCSM model. The first requisite seen needed by the teacher now is mastery of the subject matter. To achieve this mastery, Madison Project provides 30 hours of mathematics training to participating classroom teachers. Initial teaching for the Project is done either by Ph.D. mathematicians or by mathematically sophisticated teachers. This teaching is felt to be essential, not to oppose former emphasis on the importance of teacher-pupil interaction and the need to understand the pupil, but *to make such interaction possible.* In other words, the teacher's knowledge of the learner and interaction skills become operable *only if* the teacher is secure in his grasp of the subject matter. Absence or loss of this grasp inevitably is associated with inadequate interaction capability and authority-centered techniques on the part of the teacher. By itself, this inadequacy can result in systems failure. Thus the teacher must be mathematically creative, flexible, and well-educated; nonauthoritarian; able to respect children as people; capable of affection for the learner; and attentive to the learner's "needs for physical activity, attention, autonomy, etc."

The instruction input for this model is unique among present-day programs. It is a gallant effort to overcome the historic "rhetoric of conclusions" typical of past and present ESM methods and replace it by a "rhetoric of inquiry." The object is to get around the pervasive notion that every question has one right answer and that children should know what it is. Rather the emphasis lies on asking the right questions: those which stimulate discovery, invention, and, incidentally, appropriate but not necessarily expected or "right-according-to-some-authority" answers. In general, instructional methods and materials include word-of-mouth communication, interaction, audio tapes, films, text materials, and many other of the new and familiar devices created to assist teachers in the instruction of ESM. The chief emphasis is on a "low-key" approach, oriented to the pursuit of ideas. Because of the pernicious effects paper-and-pencil testing has had on instruction in the past, relatively little testing of this sort is done in the grades. Evaluation takes place during the interaction of the classroom lesson. Where tests are applied, extensive efforts are made to insure that the instruction remains "authentic," that is, oriented to the discovery of important mathematical ideas rather than testmanship. Finally, instructional management is flexible, sometimes individualized, sometimes group-oriented. It makes frequent use of the competitive nature of children in a variety of group game situations. But always, the content must be directed to some idea or process included in the list of essential content inputs. The lesson is never done simply because it's a nice thing to do with children or is interesting to do but mathematically irrelevant.

Dynamic Curriculum Models

Characteristics of a Dynamic Curriculum Model

The terms "static" and "dynamic" have been used in passing to describe curriculum models. With the Madison Project model available now as an illustration to contrast with earlier models, it is appropriate to expand on the meaning of these terms.

A static systems model, as the name implies, operates with fixed inputs and a fixed output. The nature of the output does not change with time except as random or uncontrollable factors within the system cause unexpected and unpredictable changes in the output. In the past, curriculum systems have been static systems mainly because it has not been technically possible to devise them in any other way. Thus, one decided first what optimum output was desired, then went about fixing up the inputs to achieve this. Once the system parameters were set, they remained essentially fixed. For instance, if the decision was that children should achieve mastery of certain skills by the end of a certain grade, it was left to the teachers of that grade to secure mastery in the skill but not to decide that perhaps it would be better if the skill were replaced by others or taught at some other grade level. In this way the outputs became fixed as an orthodox system became established.

However, with the rapid change in our society over the last century, the difference between the actual educational output and the needed output caused ever-increasing stresses until a cataclysmic break with the past seemed to be the only way out. Reform took place and as much as possible, a new static system replaced the old.

We have mentioned the principle of feedback in a system to control the output. The feedback which occurs within the system via the child learning from his errors or the teacher sensing needed changes during classroom interaction might be called the inner feedback loop. Within the established constraints of the static system, the inner loop operates to achieve the defined optimal output. Now the Madison Project system is to an extent novel in that it provides an outer feedback loop. This outer loop is one which over longer periods of time, of the order of school years, monitors the output of the system. Children are followed along from year to year and the inputs to the system are modified from the information collected in this manner.

The method used in curriculum construction to build this outer loop is a unique contribution of the Madison Project. Rather than define a desired output and build a complete static curriculum to produce it, the program "does something" first and then observes the effect. If desirable, the "something" is polished and kept in the curriculum. If the output is not desirable, the "something" is either dropped or modified. This modification is done by taking a "bit-and-pieces" approach to the curriculum. A sequence of lessons is built around a relevant mathematical topic, tried out, and polished. When it appears that the sequence can be taught in a practical fashion in ordinary classrooms, teachers are taught how to provide the instruction. Then like an hypodermic injection, the sequence is inserted into the existing curriculum. By making small changes in existing systems with instructional segments that can be dependably taught, the system is dynamically changed. Output over a period of months and years is observed and the input parameters adjusted regularly to produce the dynamically changing definitions of optimal output.

Our final example of a systems model of ESM curriculum is a hybrid of several projects now in progress. It illustrates how the new technology of the computer can play a role in building a dynamic ESM curriculum. In order to prevent a system from becoming frozen in a static configuration, effective feedback loops are necessary: an inner loop to optimize the immediate benefit to individuals within the system, and an outer loop to monitor the long-range total system performance. The outer loop provides the necessary data on which to base decisions to modify the system in conformance with the changing needs of our schools and society.

The Computer-Oriented ESM Curriculum

One of the most tenacious problems of curriculum construction has been to resolve conflicts caused by the demands of two seemingly opposite criteria for optimality. On the one hand, we want to preserve the uniqueness of the individual, indeed to enhance his potential for constructive use of the special gifts and abilities he possesses. On the other hand, we aspire to a certain uniform quality of educational productivity, a high quality based on the acquisition of vital and relevant knowledge as well as the favorable attitudes which encourage the exercise of that knowledge.

Two schools of curriculum thinking have developed in the past years, each one cognizant of these twin needs but emphasizing in their respective approaches one or the other criteria. The one school is man and content oriented; the other is machine-content oriented. That is, both approaches have much in common concerning the kinds of mathematics content which they regard as essential. But the former approaches instruction from a global or macroscopic point of view of human interaction, giving attention to the central, unifying ideas of content which the human mind seems to need for effective organization of information. The latter approaches instruction from an atomistic or microscopic point of view, seeking to find the hierarchies of knowledge and small step sequences by which the learners can be routed from point to point in the hierarchy of content. Each one aspires to individualize instruction but in distinctly different ways. In the former, the routes suggested by individual discovery and inquiry are spontaneous and unplanned. Nevertheless, due to the teacher's guidance, they remain closely related to the child's immediate interest and relevant to important mathematical ideas. In the latter, the child's overt behavior signals either success or failure in reaching some node or branch point in a hierarchy. At that point, a decision is made whether to send him "back" for remedial work or "forward" along some optimally chosen path to seek a goal which the system sets for him.

What is needed today is confluence of these two streams of curriculum building. One promising approach to combine the strengths of each stream lies in the utilization of recent advances in computer technology.

An ideal ESM curriculum is one which would have the following characteristics, among others:

1. Capable of continuous modification to meet local educational needs.
2. Under the control of the teacher rather than the textbook.
3. Well articulated from level to level; sequential in nature.
4. Capable of stable, high-quality educational productivity.
5. Flexible, meeting the needs of individual students.

One of the most promising approaches to this ideal today is through the use of cybernetic systems technology. A cybernetic system is basically an interacting man-machine system. One of the essential features of such a system is the optimal use of the respective capabilities of human beings and instrumentation. The goal of such a system is to produce a controllable and therefore predictable output. Obviously, system control is an essential requirement both for optimizing the output and for adapting the system to changing criteria of optimality.

Although individual human behavior is no more predictable than is the behavior of, say, an individual atom, there is no reason to believe that the behavior or educational *systems* cannot be controlled and predicted. For in the system, one has the cancellation of individual random effects through a "law of averages." Thus concern for the individual can be maintained without sacrificing system control and stability.

The essential capability of the cybernetic system which enables it to be both stable and adaptable to changing conditions is feedback. The idea itself is not new either in educational or engineering systems. Teachers have long used the results of tests and the observations which came from personal interaction with children to provide corrective feedback. In recent years, greater use has been made of programed instructional materials to provide immediate feedback or reinforcement to the learner. However, a number of technical difficulties have prevented the system from working as well as one might wish.

For the human teacher, attempts to individualize instruction run into immediate management obstacles. The human mind is not well adapted to monitoring and retaining large amounts of specific data of the kind which results from highly individualized instruction. The teacher gets the feeling the situation is getting out of hand. He does not know where the youngsters are in their study nor how well they are grasping the material. About one teacher for each pupil seems to be required to keep track of performance, an unfeasible solution in terms of available funds and manpower.

Some experiments in the last 5 years have been instituted to overcome this problem. Initially, the computer was used to take over the teacher's role in presenting the material and evaluating the pupils' responses. While interesting, these experiments have suggested a better division of labor between the teacher and the machine. Human memory works well with broad conceptual schemes. The human teacher can also utilize an impressive array of communication modes with which to interact with the learner. The chief limitation of the human mind becomes apparent when it fails under the cognitive strain imposed by demands to remember, retrieve, and manipulate large amounts of bits and pieces of data. The computer, however, is at its best in monitoring and manipulating with great accuracy such bits and pieces of data. But it has no common sense, no global grasp of affairs, and at present very limited perceptual and communicative powers. It is therefore poorly suited to direct the process of inquiry. Thus, where the human teacher excels, the computer has limited capability; and what the computer does best, the teacher finds most difficult to do. Thus the teacher and the computer are to a large extent complementary in their capabilities. This complementary nature suggests utilizing the strengths of each in a man-machine or cybernetic system of curriculum.

Such a system would be flexible enough to handle almost any forseeable kind of output expected from an ESM curriculum. The important problem to be solved is the division of labor between the man and machine. What division would optimize system performance?

Some of the research done on this question suggests that the machine is vital to the efficient functioning of the feedback loops. Essentially, it relieves the teacher from attention to many of the details of classroom management which involve data collection and manipulation. By maintaining well-organized records of student performance and personality characteristics, teacher characteristics, and available materials characteristics, the possibility exists to utilize the high-speed data-processing capability of the computer in two important ways. The first is to provide to the teacher and the pupil the kinds of data needed immediately for effective short-term management: diagnostic information on where the pupil is and how he is doing. These data constitute the inner feedback loop necessary for system control. The second is to utilize the machine's ability to retain large amounts of performance data over long periods of time to provide a basis of evaluation for educational productivity. This outer cybernetic loop is necessary for system adaptability. Thus immediate feedback enables the teacher to individualize instruction without losing control while maintaining a high quality of output. It also frees the teacher to participate in the person-to-person interaction needed to guide inquiry. The long-term feedback enables system modification to meet the demands of new kinds of content or changes in the pupil population characteristics.

Recent technological developments in computer systems which enable the computer to use its high-speed capabilities to handle many problems "simultaneously" (called time-sharing), have opened up certain possibilities in the use of computers as limited instructional devices. At Stanford University, Suppes has developed a drill-and-practice system which operates through remote teletypes which can be placed in the school.[26] The central computer, which can be located at almost any distance from the school, serves to provide the pupil with a brief arithmetic drill program tailored with respect to difficulty to the individual's abilities. This system at present is not designed for initial instruction in the basic operations, but rather for effective maintenance and remedial work in these skills as the performance of the individual indicates it is needed. More work on the potential of computer-assisted instruction is underway at the present time.

As cybernetic systems are developed, we may expect that many of the curriculum objectives that have been sought in the past will become increasingly operable. Flexible prescription systems capable of matching pupils with teacher and material as his immediate needs require will become realities. The needed key will be provided to break the lock step curriculum, replace antiquated grouping and grading practices with an efficient matching of pupils with educational resources, provide a stable and controllable curriculum, and enable the system to adapt to changing requirements. Such systems may not be far in the future.

COMPARISON OF PAST AND PROPOSED ESM CURRICULA

By describing the ESM curricula in terms of a systems model, one has available a common basis for comparing past and proposed systems. We now summarize the essential distinctions between the traditional arithmetic curriculum and "modern math."

---

[26]P. Suppes, "Tomorrow's Education? Computer-Based Instruction for the Elementary School," *Education Age*, Vol. 2, No. 3 (January-February) 1966. See also P. Suppes, *et al.*, *Arithmetic Drills and Review on a Computer-Based Teletype*, Technical Report No. 83 (Stanford: Institute for Mathematical Studies in the Social Sciences, November 5, 1965).

The idealized learner input to the curriculum—those imputed characteristics of the child which are directly considered in planning his learning experiences—has experienced a major redesign. The essential shift is in the direction from pragmatist to intellectual. Neither extreme, of course, has ever been or ever will be *the* view of the learner. Rather, a balance between the two extreme views is desirable. Formerly, the balance point favored the pragmatic side; recent recommendations have argued strongly for shifting the equilibrium point to favor the intellectual qualities.

Thus the new emphasis in the system output is on mathematical self-reliance, a state of mind for which the necessary preparation is a unified and comprehensive grasp of the structure of centrally important mathematical systems.

Accordingly, the content input is undergoing a change in its characteristics. Where the former emphasis was on practical skills and processes, the new stress rests on ideas which the mathematician regards as fundamental: the structure of the real number system, certain aspects of geometry, and the basic schemes of logical inference. These kinds of ideas, as we saw in Chapter 1, are precisely those which lie at the heart of the last hundred years of mathematical progress. Hence, the term *modern math*.

The redesign of the learner and content input interacts strongly with the teacher and instructional inputs. The new curricula place very heavy demands on the teachers' knowledge of content. This shift from the past is fundamental; attention had been centered on the knowledge of child. Again, one or another extreme adjustment of this parameter is not being advocated. Rather adjustments need to be made to obtain the kind of balance which contributes to optimizing the output. The systems approach should help take this issue out of the realm of doctrinaire debate and place it in an objective perspective: The system parameters are adjusted to produce optimal output, not to conform to a predetermined school of thought.

Instruction has experienced extreme adjustments in the past 50 years. This parameter has been pushed to one extreme or another in the hope of optimizing output. For arithmetic, the actual output has remained at a relatively constant, unsatisfactorily low level rather independent of the adjustments made in methods, management, and materials. This low level has been partly due to the fact that one parameter usually does not determine the output. It is the outstanding example of the cause of past systems failures. Many of the methods advocated in the past nevertheless make good sense when the other inputs are properly designed and adjusted. This fact explains why methods which seem not to have worked well in the past may still prove to be very appropriate. The fact that attention has been riveted excessively on this one input does not render the input defective, but rather implies that the system as a whole has been out of adjustment. The proposed new curricula are attempting to redesign the other inputs appropriately. In so doing, many former parameters may well be found to be critically related to an optimized output. Instruction emphasizing flexible grouping, inquiry, discovery, and the use of concrete materials is a prime example of this.

Topics for Further Investigation

1. Construct a model of the arithmetic curriculum as you recall it from your own grade school experience. Since it is probable that some aspects of the several models sketched in this chapter will be found in the one you construct, try to identify the sources of the components you build into your model. If you went through many kinds of curricula, pick one year that you recall best and build a model for that year.

2. Construct a model of an ESM curriculum that you believe you might be able to use as a teacher in some grade K to 6. Defend your definition of optimal output. Also suggest a brief rationale for the input parameters you choose to stress or de-emphasize. If you have a special interest such as teaching culturally deprived children or the behaviorally disabled, include your special consideration in the learner input to your model.

3. Construct an ideal ESM model for the future as you visualize it. What implications do you see in your model for teacher training? How much mathematics, estimated in terms of credit hours, do you see teachers of ESM having in the future? What are the pros and cons of elementary school teachers having content specialities?

4. What trends do you see in mathematics instruction for the young over the last 50 years? Has any of our thinking about teaching ESM developed by building on knowledge gained in the past (linear development) or has it been mainly in the nature of first knocking down former ideas and replacing them with totally new ones?

5. Look up some programed materials for teaching arithmetic. In what form do you find "feedback" in this kind of material?

6. How might computers be used as feedback links in a typical kind of classroom setting?

7. Do you think it possible for computers to replace teachers? Try to defend your position from a systems point of view.

8. Would you characterize teaching ESM as a science primarily, or an art? Possibly you may take an intermediate position; if so, spell out your view of the art and science aspects of teaching.

9. Do you think a beginning teacher should attempt to teach mathematical ideas by a method of Socratic inquiry? If yes, specify the qualifications you feel your education must provide to enable you to do this. If not, what are some suitable alternatives?

10. Did Thorndike advocate that a teacher should explain *why* a process worked before the children were skilled in it? Or did he advocate developing skill by example without providing the rationale? Do you consider the method he advocated to be inductive teaching? Was it teaching by discovery?

11. In what respect did the meaningful theorists of the 1940's and 1950's employ the terms *meaningful* and *insightful?* Do you think the CCSM authors refer to the same thing when they refer to mathematical meaning or insight?

12. What is your position on the validity of Social Utility Theory as it applies to ESM instruction? Is social utility the main reason for teaching arithmetic today? If yes, defend your position. If not, what is the primary reason for mathematics in the curriculum?

13. What is your own position on the potential intrinsic interest that mathematics has for most people? Do you think it is considered dull stuff by most children?

14. Should children be encouraged to do scratch work separately and hand in only the answers? Should the "correct" form of the answer be specified by the teacher or left to the child to decide? Defend your position.

15. What role should class projects play in mathematics instruction, in your view? What do you see as the advantages and disadvantages of this technique?

16. Do you think typical problems found in ESM textbooks are of a "real-life" nature? If yes, give examples. If not, can you suggest ways of finding true-to-life problems that will fit into the limited time available for math instruction?

17. Is time devoted to math instruction a parameter of the curriculum model? If yes, to which input does it seem to belong? If not, how does it relate to the model?

18. What administrative policies of a school would be considered as important constraints affecting the optimum output of an ESM model? List some of the practical constraints you see that might make the CCSM model ineffective at this time.

19. Choose a textbook series for ESM and construct a model of curriculum compatible with the point of view represented in the text. Can one model fit all grades K-6, or only a single grade, or some set of grades? Try to characterize the model by comparing it with those discussed in this chapter.

Bibliography

Adler, I. "The Cambridge Report: Blueprint or Fantasy?" *The Mathematics Teacher*, 59 (3):210-17, March, 1966.

Ausubel, D. P., and D. Fitzgerald. "Organizer, General Bacground, and Antecedent Learning Variables in Sequential Verbal Learning," *Journal of Educational Psychology*, 33 (1962), 243-249.

Baker, F. B. "Use of Computers in Educational Research," *Review of Educational Research*, December, 1963, 566-578.

Biddle, B. J. "The Integration of Teacher Effectiveness Research," in B. J. Biddle and W. J. Ellena (eds.), *Contemporary Research on Teacher Effectiveness*. New York: Holt, Rinehart and Winston, Inc., 1964, 1-40.

Borko, Harold (ed.). *Computer Applications in the Behavioral Sciences*. Englewood Cliffs, N.J.: Prentice-Hall, 1962.

Brueckner, L. J., and F. E. Grossnickle. *Making Arithmetic Meaningful*. Philadelphia: The John C. Winston Company, 1953.

Buck, R. C. "Goals for Mathematics Instruction," *The American Mathematical Monthly*, 72 (1965), 949-956.

Bushnell, D. D. "For Each Student a Teacher," *Saturday Review*, 49(30).

Cahern, L. S. "An Interim Report on the National Longitudinal Study of Mathematics Abilities," *The Mathematics Teacher*, 63 (1965), 522-526.

Cambridge Conference on School Mathematics. *Goals for School Mathematics*.

Coulson, John E. (ed.). *Programmed Learning and Computer-Based Instruction*. New York: John Wiley & Sons, 1962.

Davis, R. B. *The Changing Curriculum: Mathematics*. Association for Supervision and Curriculum Development, Washington, D.C.: The Association, 1967.

_____. "The Madison Project's Approach to a Theory of Instruction," *Journal of Research in Science Teaching,* 2 (1964), 146-162.

DeVault, M. Vere. "What Is Mathematics Curriculum Research?" *The Arithmetic Teacher,* 13:636-639.

Feigenbaum, E. A., and J. Feldman (eds.). *Computers and Thought.* New York: McGraw-Hill Book Company, Inc., 1963.

Fogel, L. J., et al. *Artificial Intelligence through Simulated Evolution.* New York: John Wiley & Sons, Inc., 1966.

Goodlad, J., et al. *The Changing School Curriculum.* New York: The Fund for the Advancement of Education, 477 Madison Avenue, 1966.

Goodlad, J. I., J. O'Toole, and L. L. Tyler. *Computers and Information Systems in Education.* New York: Harcourt, Brace and World, 1966.

Hawkins, David. "Childhood and the Education of Intellectuals," *Harvard Educational Review,* 36(4):477-83, Fall, 1966.

Macdonald, J. B., and J. D. Raths. "Curriculum Research: Problems, Techniques and Prospects," *Review of Educational Research,* 33:322-329.

Ryans, D. G. *Characteristics of Teachers.* Washington, D.C.: American Council on Education, 1960.

Schwab, J. J. "The Teaching of Science as Enquiry," in J. J. Schwab and Brandwein, *The Teaching of Science.* Cambridge, Mass.: Harvard University Press, 1964.

Stone, M. H. "Review of Goals for School Mathematics: The Report of the Cambridge Conference on School Mathematics," *The Mathematics Teacher,* 58(4):353-60, April, 1965.

Suchman, J. R. *Developing Inquiry.* Chicago: Science Research Associates, Inc., 1966.

Suppes, P. *Computer-Assisted Instruction in the Schools: Potentialities, Problems, Prospects.* Technical Report No. 81, Psychology Series. Stanford: Institute for Mathematical Studies in the Social Sciences, October 29, 1965.

_____. "The Uses of Computers in Education," *Scientific American,* Vol. 215, No. 3, September, 1966, 206-220.

Suppes, P., et al. *Arithmetic Drills and Review on a Computer-Based Teletype.* Technical Report No. 83, Psychology Series. Stanford: Institute for Mathematical Studies in the Social Sciences, November 5, 1965.

Thorndike, Edward L. *The Psychology of Arithmetic.* New York: The Macmillan Company, 1922.

4

SYSTEMATIZING THE GROWTH OF ESM CURRICULUM

In vain the sage, with retrospective eye,
Would from the apparent What conclude the Why,
Infer the motive from the deed, and show,
That what we chanced, was what we meant to do.
Alexander Pope, Epistle I, 1733

Overview of a Pattern for Decision Making

In a period of transition such as that which ESM is undergoing today, a teacher's normal concern about the right thing to do and the best way of doing it can become a serious and worrisome matter. Once a certain comfort could be taken from the fact that a general concensus obtained with respect to content, methods, and specific points of emphasis, but the present scene often appears to be one in which it is every man for himself. Advice is abundant but conflicting. Classroom practice bridges a broader spectrum of activities than ever before. Innovation apparently knows no bounds. The diversity of views presented in ESM textbooks seems to increase with each year's new editions. How, in all this change, can a systematic decision-making process be instituted that treats the learner to a unified, consistent, up-to-date mathematics curriculum?

The answer to this question can be found in the analysis of two complementary sets of decisions. The first set has to do with the long-range determination of the course of study. This kind of curriculum construction includes, among other things, the selection of that mathematics content deemed most worth knowing. Although such decisions are not made unilaterally by the individual teacher, we include them in our consideration because of our commitment to the principle that the mathematics curriculum is everything for which the teacher is responsible as it relates to the mathematics learning of his students. In particular, the teacher's values relevant to important content ideas can strongly affect the selection of topics which receive consideration and emphasis in the daily instruction.

The second set of decisions takes place in the context provided by the long-term curriculum planning. These short-range decisions include the instructional plans made by the teacher or teaching team to provide appropriate learning experiences for the individual children, experiences which, of course, should be closely related to the long-term curricular objectives.

Figure 4-1 provides an overview of this decision-making process in the form of a flow chart. It serves as an outline of the main questions that must be decided, who should be involved in the decision making, the order in which the decision ought to be made, and the interrelationship of the various parts of the decision process to the whole ESM curriculum.

Diagram 4-1 is derived from a consideration of the systems model of curriculum developed in the last chapter.[1] Before attempting a detailed analysis of curricular and instructional decision for ESM, consider first the general features of this decision-making pattern.

Three basic decision points are indicated in the boxes labeled (1), (2), and (3). The first two are included in the set of long-term or curriculum plans (I). These decisions deal primarily with the determination of a basic content and sequence which is to be developed over the period of years from K-12. Thus we have indicated in (A) that the teachers of elementary, junior high, and senior high schools all have an important place in formulating these decisions, as do also the

---

[1]Cf. Figure 3-1.

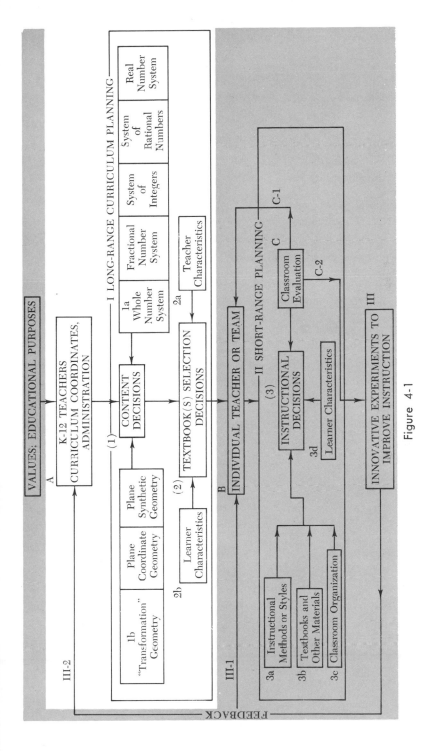

Figure 4-1

An ESM Curriculum Decision Model.

school or district's curriculum coordinators, certain administrative personnel, and perhaps certain other consultants such as those the State Department of Public Instruction or other educational resources may be able to provide. These decisions are shown in the diagram as being made in the context of local educational purposes and values. The content options which one has to choose from are indicated in the boxes in 1a and 1b.

The determination of content decisions generates the criteria needed for selecting textbooks, as indicated in (2). The boxes in 2a and 2b indicate subsidiary considerations that affect textbook selection decisions: the learner's characteristics and the teacher's characteristics. In the case of the learner, such things as reading level, attractiveness, and format of the text will be considered. As for the teacher, his mathematical knowledge or need to improve content knowledge may influence the particular choice of text. The need to effect economies in time required for planning may also cause greater emphasis to be placed on securing textbooks having guides which suggest such things as appropriate supplementary materials to be used with lessons, suitable enrichment activities, or other helps needed to handle special learning problems that may arise.

The two important decisions made in the process of long-range curriculum planning—(1) determination of comprehensive but clearly circumscribed content objectives, and (2) selection of suitable textbooks which constitute the primary materials which embody these objectives—are decisions which establish the needed context for teachers or teams to plan systematically the daily learning experiences for their students.

The long-term decisions are linked to the short-range planning (II) in two important ways. First of all, the teachers (B) keep the content objectives in mind to guide their instructional decision making (3). Second, the textbook (3b) provides the basic sequence for the content to be communicated to the learner.

The *teacher* or team must decide on the kind of methods (3a) which are most appropriate to the day's lesson. In this regard, he must also consider the characteristics of the particular learners (3d) whom he will teach, their needs, interests, abilities, motivation, and so on. Finally, he must make provision to evaluate (3c) both the learning output and the quality of the instruction with due regard for both long- and short-range objectives.

Ideas for the next planning steps come about through two kinds of feedback. The inner loop (C1) is the feedback obtained directly by the teacher or team during interaction with the learners during the classroom lesson. Certain ideas for improving the very next lesson or lessons will be incorporated as a result of such on-the-spot evaluation. Evaluation will also reveal the existence of certain persistent instructional problems which do not seem to yield to any established instructional techniques. These problems become the basis for innovative experimentation (III) which either yields the kind of instructional breakthrough that enables the objectives in question to be attained or indicates that within the present state of the art such objectives are not satisfactorily attainable.

In this way, the feedback from the innovative experiments contributes to both the short-term (III-1) and long-term (III-2) decision process. First, successful new techniques must be taught to the teachers in order that their repertoire of instructional skills can be enlarged. Second, the knowledge of what *can* be successfully taught and what cannot, within the state of the art, must modify the long-range decisions regarding what *should* be taught. In this way, theoretical ideals are adjusted to the realistic constraints of teaching skills and technology. In addition, the gradual accumulation of instructional knowledge enables the ESM curriculum to grow in a steady and stable manner, thus providing the dynamic characteristics so desired for the curriculum as well as a stable frame of reference in which to provide a systematic, sequential set of learning experiences for the learners.

After these remarks on the general nature of the problems and decisions associated with systematizing the growth of ESM curriculum and instruction, we now examine alternatives and consequences of decisions that might be reached with regard to the four inputs to the curriculum: content, instruction, teacher, and learner.

THE FIRST DECISIONS: CONTENT OBJECTIVES

ESM curriculum builders have long been troubled with concerns relating to the comparative importance of various parts of the curriculum. We see these concerns manifested in the use of such terms as the *content-centered curriculum*, the *child-centered curriculum*, and such slogans as "Teach children, not mathematics." It is important that these anachronisms be laid to rest.

We have chosen a systems point of view regarding curriculum in order that each component may be seen in proper perspective and be given due consideration. This point of view needs to be emphasized because we begin by examining content, not out of the conviction that it is first in value or importance but rather because it is a necessary place to begin if one is to build a good ESM curriculum.

Perhaps a simple analogy best conveys what this does and does not imply.

In the operation of any reasonably complex system, of which the ESM curriculum is certainly an example, priority must be given to the order in which decisions are made and executed to achieve system operation. For instance, in a television system, one must produce the signal before it can be received. Without a signal, no amount of manipulation of receiver controls, tuning, fine tuning, volume increase, contrast adjustment, and the like can have any significant effect on the output. In the absence of a clear signal transmitted with minimum distortion to the receiver, receiver adjustments modify only the raster that is internally generated by the set.

In the analogous ESM curriculum, the place to begin decision making is not with the transmission link—the textbook or methods—nor with the receiver—the child—but rather with a clear conception of the content—the message or signal—that is to be transmitted to the child in some clear fashion. Once the content is determined, one tunes up the system to minimize distortion, maintain the receiver's efficiency, periodically check on its performance, and so on.

In other words, curriculum planning should begin with decisions regarding that input which is the unique source of inquiry for the particular curriculum in question, rather than the components such as learner, teacher, or instruction which are general features of all curricula.

Then the instructional decisions, the methods, materials, and means of evaluation, can be rationally decided. These decisions in turn appropriately take into account the teacher's roles and goals as well as the immediate and long-range needs of the child.

The Basic Parameters of ESM Content

Beginning with the content input, then, we need to identify those stable, easily remembered, long-range content characteristics which serve to guide and test the relevance of daily instructional planning. We wish to outline five such characteristics. Sometimes characteristics of this sort are called content "strands;" in the terminology of our systems model, we call them *parameters* of the content input. They are in various degrees common to all past ESM curricula and are a part of the projected curricula. A clear conception of the basic content parameters provides a stable frame of reference which not only simplifies decision making but enables one to see unity and consistency in what otherwise might appear to be complexity and chaos.

Perhaps the easiest way to illustrate the five essential parameters which permit one to adjust the ESM curriculum to fit virtually any set of values or purposes is to examine the ESM textbooks that are commonly used in the grades. From such a study, one finds a sequence of development that occurs repeatedly. First one begins with a category or *universe* of ideas, such as whole number concepts, for example. As this universe of number ideas is developed through appropriate experiences, certain symbols are agreed upon which refer to individual elements in the universe under study. In this *symbolization* step, children learn to recognize and respond with the appropriate signs and sounds needed to communicate the ideas. As fluency in communication develops, the child begins to study *relations* which exist between elements in the universe. For instance, in early mathematics instruction, children learn that an idea may be named in many ways and any two names for the same idea are related by the = symbol. Next, certain *operations* are defined and the children learn to "operate" on and with the ideas which comprise the universe of discourse. They also learn to perform and express these operations symbolically in the form of algorithms or computational procedures. Finally, these learning experiences lead the pupils to explore the general properties of the universe under consideration together with the operations defined on it—such things as commutativity, associativity, closure, and so on. Such general properties of a universe and its defined operations are often called the "structural" properties of the system. This entire assemblage—universe, operations, and structural properties—is sometimes called a *structure* or *system*, such as the whole number system.

It is easy to see that the content input to the ESM curriculum could be defined by specifying the "settings" of each of these parameters: which structures one wants to develop during the K-12 years or any subset of grades; then, which number universes or geometric universe must be developed; the degree and kind of symbolization skill desired; and which relations and operations need to be developed, generalized, and abstracted.

From these five parameters we build what we call the basic sequence of the ESM curriculum. Figure 4-2 lists the five parameters in the basic content sequence common to all ESM curricula.

A Note on Terminology

Certain terms which cover a wide range of referents are used frequently in discussions of the ESM curriculum. In order to better serve the cause of clarity in this discussion, we pause to describe the particu-

| 1. Universe | 2. Symbolization | 3. Relation | 4. Operation | 5. Structure |

Figure 4-2

The Basic Content Sequence

lar usage employed in this text of such terms as *system, structure, model; idea, concept, principle,* and *law.*

Of the first group—system, structure, and model—*system* is the most inclusive label. It refers in general to an organization of parts into an interrelated whole. We have referred to the curriculum as a system composed of certain interrelated parts—content, instruction, and so on. We may also use the same term to refer to a *number system,* for instance. Such a system would consist of a *universe* of number ideas, like rational numbers; one or more *operations,* such as addition or multiplication; and certain statements which describe the logical *properties* of the number system with respect to the defined operations. Another example of the use of the term *system* occurs in connection with a *numeration system.* This system consists of a set of interrelated agreements or conventions designed to express number names in a compact and efficient manner. Our familiar decimal numeration system is one illustration. The Roman numeration system is another.

Going back to the case of number system, the reader may recall that such a system provides a framework for deducing true statements about the system. The mathematician tends to think of the basic properties—such as commutativity, associativity, and so on—as *axioms,* and the true statements which are obtained deductively from these as *theorems.* In other words, axioms are accepted true statements; theorems require proof before their truth value can be assigned.

However, in the elementary grades, we do not as yet find the use of the words *axiom* and *theorem* commonplace. They probably sound too formal and formidable to most teachers. Consequently, less precise terms are used as synonyms. Instead of speaking of the Axiom of Commutativity, we prefer to refer to it as the Commutative Principle or the Commutative Law. Although some authors attempt to reserve *law* as a synonym for *axiom,* and *principle* as a synonym for *theorem,* the usage in the literature is not consistent. On occasion the word *property* may be used in place of law or principle, such as the commutative property of addition. In most cases, the intent of the word used can be gained from the context and little confusion arises from the interchangeable use of the words principle, property, or law. Axioms and theorems are not the same thing but we shall have infrequent need to use these terms. We will keep the distinction between the two clear whenever they are used.

A *structure*, in much of the mathematical usage of the term, refers to a *deductive system*. For the reader who has had some contact with modern algebra, a Group or a Ring or a Field serves as an immediate example of a mathematical structure. A number system may be a *particular example* or *model* of such a structure.[2] We will have little occasion to refer to the abstract, general kind of deductive system which the mathematician thinks of as a structure. However, certain terms in common use which we will have to use arise from the mathematical concept of structure.

Rather than use the terms *structure* and *model* as the mathmatician might prefer, we will find it easier to refer to the particular number systems found in the grades as structures rather than models. In other words, the familiar system of {whole numbers, defined operations, and properties of the operations} serves as an example of what we will term a *structure*. Then it makes some sense to talk of *structural properties* as statements which our intuition or reason suggests are true about the particular structure.

In the foregoing sense then, we can consider not only arithmetic structure but also geometry in any one of its various forms as a structure. For instance, one may select a universe of objects—such as points, lines, and planes—on which operations such as translation or rotation or stretching may be defined. We can accept certain statements as being true—"a straight line is the shortest distance between two points"—and others we may intuit or prove to be true about the system —for example, "the sum of the interior angles of a triangle is a straight angle." In general, the term *structure* serves to refer to any of the central mathematical systems which form the long-range framework of the mathematics curriculum K-12.

Eric Temple Bell has compared the mathematician's concept of structure with a waltz form in music.[3] The structure is the form of *all* waltzes, so to speak, and a model is a particular waltz. For the mathematician, a structure is a powerful unifying idea inasmuch as it gives him the power to reason about many particular models in one fell swoop. In a manner of speaking, he can do all waltzes at once. The economy of thought, the power of analysis, the practical fruit of this

[2]Reference V. H. Haag, *Structure of Algebra* (Reading, Mass.: Addison-Wesley Publishing Company, 1964).

[3]E. T. Bell, *Mathematics: Queen and Servant of Science* (New York: McGraw-Hill Book Company, Inc., 1951), p. 45.

abstract reasoning, and the beauty and elegance of such thinking all contribute greatly to the value of mathematics and mathematics study.

Because all of these qualities which are related to good mathematical thinking are important cognitive ideals which guide the entire K-12 mathematics program, one finds increasing emphasis in the new programs on "structural concepts," "unifying ideas," and so on.

Finally, *idea* is used to refer to almost any mental construct. It is a broad term signifying some object of our thought. A *concept* is usually employed to refer to some particular category of ideas, such as a number concept. Occasionally, one finds the word *principle* used in connection with a particular mechanical procedure, such as this principle for dividing fractions: "Invert the divisor and multiply." In this usage, *principle* is synonymous with *rule* or *procedure*. In most cases involving these words, the context will make them clear.

In this present era in which so much is made of the precise use of language, one must be careful not to go from one extreme of fuzziness to the other of hair-splitting. We need to agree on what the terms mean in the context of school mathematics and, as much as possible, keep the meaning of commonly used terms related to the special usage which the child may encounter in later mathematics study. However, it is necessary to start using language in a very approximate manner with young children, stressing the intuitive aspects rather than formal definitions. Arnold Ross has called this method teaching by an abuse of language. It is not only a good way to begin instruction, but the only way. Gradual refinements can and should come as the child experiences the need to refine the use of terms. The ultimate test by which our use of language must be judged is the test of clarity in communication. The terms, symbols, and words we use must, above all, be clear to the children we teach and, therefore, must be adapted constantly to *their* developing level of communication skill.

Selecting the Content Objectives

We have suggested that the first decisions must be in regard to long-range content objectives. In terms of the five parameters of the basic sequences, what is the nature of the particular decisions that must be made? In what order should decisions regarding the choice of universes, the level of symbolization, the treatment of relations, of operations, and structures be decided? Who should decide and what are the effects of alternative decisions?

The selection of a good textbook series might appear to be an easy answer. Twenty years ago, perhaps even 10 or 5 years back, that decision was probably as effective as any. It is less appropriate today and will become less so in the future.

The reason lies in the fact that, in the past, the content of arithmetic textbooks was essentially one and the same. In Chapter 3, we indicated that the traditional number systems included whole numbers and fractions, considerable stress on the base-ten numeration system of symbolization and associated algorithms, primary stress on equality and virtual indifference to inequalities, the four fundamental operations, and limited applications of these ideas to social and business problems.

The trend that began in discussion during the mid-1950's and which now is appearing in many textbook series has been to extend mathematical experiences considerably. A glance at Table 1 on page 32-3, under the column headed "Summary of Basic Purposes," reveals the nature of the trend. The new ESM curricula, while diverse in many important ways, share in common the *shift from a social basis* of curriculum construction to one which emphasizes mathematical *structures*, in our sense of the term.

The effect of this trend on the decisions that must be made is of the following nature. Since the time allotted to ESM instruction in the curriculum is relatively fixed, varying between about 30 to 50 minutes a day in most schools, the inclusion of additional number systems or geometric models forces one to be selective. Although some groups, such as CCSM, have proposed radical reorganization of the content to begin with integers and proceed to real numbers and geometry rather quickly, tradition has given whole numbers and fractions a firm place in the curriculum. At the present time, the tendency is to sandwich selected new structures in among the traditional ones.

Unfortunately, from the learner's point of view, this can give rise to inefficient learning experiences. From the teacher's point of view, it seems that the number of mathematics programs to choose from is excessive with little reason for selecting one over another. A clear sense of purpose becomes difficult to maintain. One may be reduced to the last resort of having to "teach the text" that happens to be in the child's hands at the moment. Frequently, one is unable to count on the child having learned much about some of the newer material, such as sets or "signed numbers" (integers) in his past experience. It is equally difficult to know whether or not the content presently being learned will be systematically developed in subsequent grades.

This kind of problem no textbook can, of itself, solve, nor can a general prescription be provided. The staff of the local school system must determine, in the light of local values and purposes, answers to the following questions: What particular number systems and geometric structures ought to be included in the child's learning experiences? In what order should these occur and at what approximate age or grade level or ability level should they be introduced? Once these questions have been answered, one has established both the ESM curriculum and the criteria necessary to choose a textbook series that best incorporates the scope and sequence decided upon.

Thus, of the five content parameters, the first that needs to be decided upon is related to structure. After this general determination is made, successively more particular decisions follow rather naturally. Our purpose is not to *make* the choice. However, we can suggest what should be considered in making such decisions and also what the consequences may be if such matters are left to chance.

Fundamentally, curriculum decisions regarding which structure will or will not be emphasized in the K-6 curriculum must be concerned with three basic options. The most conservative decision would be to restrict content considerations to the structures of what some used to call "arithmetic." These structures would include one or more of the following systems: the system of natural numbers, of whole numbers, of fractions, of integers, or of rational numbers.

In general, each of these systems can be developed out of the learners' experiences involving the *counting* of *discrete objects*. One is able to employ the teaching techniques based on rudimentary measurement—counting—which experience has shown most children respond to very well.

The most radical decision would be to extend mathematical learning experiences to include the structures of what some once called "mathematics." Most importantly for the grades, the system of real numbers would be included. This system is fundamentally associated with the notion of *continuity* as contrasted with the *discrete* characteristics of the "arithmetic" structures.

While the mathematical importance of the real number system is such that consideration should be given to ways and means of readying the pupil to learn about it, at the moment unresolved pedagogical obstacles block the path to this objective. The traditional counting or measurement approach is both logically and psychologically appealing only to the point of developing fractional or rational number concepts. The approximate nature of measurement which always permits "rounding off" to a nearby rational number value neither serves to motivate the need for real numbers nor does it suggest much about their essential structure. One is forced, pedagogically, to make a break from a measurement approach to an analytical approach. This approach involves both the use of logic and such concepts as convergent sequences of rational numbers. It is not clear as yet what the earliest age or ability level is for developing real number concepts. Little is being done at present at the elementary level in this regard except on an innovative or experimental basis.

The third option is something of a shotgun approach. Since the nature of the mathematics learning the child may actually experience at the higher grade levels or, for that matter, which children will elect to pursue mathematics study beyond grade 9 or 10, is difficult to predict, one might attempt to broaden rather than deepen the earlier mathematical experiences. To this end, the structures selected may deal a little with the ideas of continuity and real numbers, with selected topics from geometry, measurement, or probability, and to a large extent with the familiar arithmetic structures.

It appears that many textbook authors are selecting this middle ground while waiting out the determination of the direction ESM may take in the future. Thus one finds some geometry included in many texts, topics from probability and statistics, applications to science, various degrees of emphasis on the algebra of sets, as well as the traditional topics of whole numbers and fractions.

Selection of this option, while offering some advantages, places the greatest demands on curriculum planners to articulate the program, to see that selected content is learned for a better purpose than the fact that it just happens to be on the next page of the textbook.

While mathematically adequate, teachable, sequential curriculum can possibly be built out of the "shotgun" approach, the need for frequent exchange of ideas among the K-12 staff is greatly increased. In the absence of such interaction, the program can easily degenerate into bits and pieces of material presented without real purpose, without adequate provision for the child's readiness, without provision for later systematic development, and with inappropriate and disproportionate emphasis on whatever topics most strongly attract a teacher's interest.

To avoid this degeneration, a concensus among the teachers regarding the structures to be emphasized in ESM is a necessary prerequisite for cooperative, articulated teaching. If one decides, for example, that the systems of whole numbers, of coordinate geometry, and of rational numbers deserve the main emphasis in ESM, the K-6 teachers can be *systematically* selective in providing learning experiences related primarily to these structures. Even though the children may be grouped for good sociological reasons by age into a grade for instruction, the clear goals provided by such a consensus on structures will enable the teacher to differentiate instruction more effectively. The child able to forge ahead can maintain purposeful, goal-directed progress while at the same time learning to think divergently, to inquire within the realm of the basic structures. There is less need, less pressure to hold some pupils back while prodding others on, perhaps beyond the limit of their ability. Evaluation of the learners' progress can also be made according to criteria related to long-range objectives rather than the short-range criteria for mastery in grade level that has typified much of past practice.

Selecting Textbooks

Figure 4-1 shows textbook decisions following content decisions. In this section, we want to explore what such decisions involve. A brief account of the mechanics of textbook selection is given first, raising some questions concerning the role that teachers have or ought to have in the selection process. After a brief consideration of the teacher's role in the decision-making process, the important features desirable in a textbook series are outlined. These features are incorporated in an illustrative checklist which suggests a systematic method of choosing textbooks for classroom use. The matter of how to use textbooks in an appropriate fashion is deferred to the next section.

The Mechanics of Adoption

Textbooks adoptions are typically made in one of three ways. We may call these (1) the single-state adoption, (2) the multiple-state adoption, and (3) open adoption. In the first instance, a state adoption committee selects a single text series to be purchased with state financial aids by *all* public schools in the state. In the multiple-state adoption, the committee approves a list of perhaps five series. Then each local district may adopt and purchase any that it chooses from the list. The third alternative, termed open adoption, permits each district to make its own independent decision concerning the choice of texts.

Typically, the textbooks are adopted for a period of about 5 years. "Work texts" in grades K-2 are usually of the soft-cover variety which permit children to write directly in the books. From grade 3 up, the "textbooks" are normally hard cover and may be accompanied by the use of special purpose, expendable, soft-cover "workbooks."

The Role of the Teacher in Textbook Selection

This brief consideration of mechanics raises the question of the role of the teacher in selecting texts. From all appearances, the decisions are made for the teacher by a committee somewhere at the state or district level. Do teachers influence the selection of textbooks?

The answer is that they *do*, but possibly not as directly as they might. One piece of evidence that suggests the manner in which teachers influence selection is reported by Professor Davis in his paper, *The Next Few Years*.[4] Commenting on the results of a poll that one major publisher had taken of its sales staff, Davis writes that the experienced sales representatives of that company "believed that teachers would accept only books that looked 90 per cent or more familiar. This group argued that sales can only be made with books that have the trappings of modernity—the words 'Discovery Edition' on the cover and so on—while remaining entirely traditional, or nearly so, in their actual content and approach."

First of all, this evidence indicates that teachers' attitudes concerning textbooks are reflected in the kind of textbooks actually produced. In effect, the choice available to the selection committees is limited to books which are on the whole generally acceptable to the classroom teachers.

If the reported poll is typical, however, it suggests that modern mathematics program development is limited to a shallow tokenism rather than significant content development. Other evidence reveals that this is not actually the case. Teachers have been receptive in large measure to many of the new ideas which have been introduced in recent years. However, the natural tendency is to prefer the textbook one has been using. For one reason, familiarity with the text makes it possible to effect important savings in the time needed to prepare lessons. The adoption of new texts requires certain adjustments to be made which, at first, incline the teacher's favor toward the old text. However, by the end of the new adoption period, most teachers usually have a favorable attitude toward the text, even if the change in content from the previous one involved something more than token change. Thus, progress is not being necessarily held back by the inflexibility of teachers' attitudes as some have supposed, but more likely by an overcautious interpretation of their natural inclination to conserve time and energy.

---

[4]R. B. Davis, "The Next Few Years," *The Arithmetic Teacher*, 13(5):355-62, May, 1966.

While it may be true that by their attitudes teachers exert their major, although indirect, influence on textbook publication and selection, their influence may develop in more direct ways in the future.

Probably every teacher has a favorite subject or two. For some, this favorite is mathematics. Perhaps as a result of this special interest, many classroom teachers have become very active in the development of new mathematics programs. In the course of making this contribution, they have kept abreast of new developments in ESM by reading professional periodicals, such as *The Arithmetic Teacher*. Very likely, such teachers have taken advantage of opportunities to strengthen their mathematics background and have developed a better-than-average mastery of the new mathematics content. Complementing this subject matter fluency, they have developed a sound professional foundation in terms of their knowledge of the needs and interests of children as well as familiarity with the practical limits of what is possible to do in the classroom. Such teachers should be alert for opportunities to participate in the deliberations of textbook selection committees.

In recent years, experience has indicated that new mathematics programs have been developed most effectively through the cooperation of mathematicians, mathematics educators, and elementary school-teachers. The combination of strengths which each brings to the task might similarly be expected to work well in the textbook selection process. Perhaps the future will see more of this cooperative effort than typically has been the case in the past. Certainly such a coalition would have great promise of yielding important gains in textbook quality.

Important Textbook Features

What does and what does not make a good ESM textbook has been a much-discussed topic over the years. The criteria by which texts are selected have shifted just as the objectives of ESM have changed in recent years. An illustration of the direction of change can be seen in Figure 4-3. The headings of two textbook checklists are shown, the first published in 1951 and the second in 1967.

A comparison of the two lists shows that while many of the earlier ideas regarding the criteria by which texts are selected remain pertinent, the impact of such experimental groups as are listed in Table 1 of Chapter 1 has served to bring an important new emphasis to textbooks which must now be considered.

1951	*1967*
I. Method of Presentation	I. Philosophy of Program
II. Grade Placement of Subject Matter	II. Key Content and Behavioral Objectives
III. Problems	III. Methodology Suggested for Program
IV. Provision for Individual Differences	IV. Supplementary Aids to Program
V. Testing and Remedial Measures	V. Physical Format of Book
VI. Authorship	
VII. Physical Features of Book	
VIII. Supplementary Considerations	

Figure 4-3

COMPARISON OF TEXTBOOK CHECKLISTS FROM 1951 AND 1967

In particular, the content considerations of the kind described in the previous sections have taken precedence over concerns with methodology in the list of criteria. This shift in concerns provides an improved basis for making textbook selection decisions, certainly. If it is decided, for instance, that measurement concepts, integral and rational numbers, and coordinate geometry will receive the main emphasis in the K-12 mathematics curriculum, then textbooks can be selected which deal most effectively with these structures. If, on the other hand, the real number system together with certain ideas from topology, set theory, and probability are selected for primary development, quite a different selection would be made.

Inasmuch as time is insufficient to treat thoroughly all possible structures that may be important in later mathematics study, the content decisions become critically important. The choice of textbook to fit these decisions can strongly effect the efficiency of the resulting ESM curriculum.

Failure to establish clear structural content objectives prior to textbook selection leads to a result much like turning on the television and picking the channel to view without consulting the program guide first. One *may* be satisfied with the resulting program. But the chances are great that the choice may not be the best available at the time.

We may also remark that certain frequently mentioned matters are *not* particularly critical in textbook selection. For instance, emphasis on methods employed *in the text* are relatively less important than they are usually made to appear. Actually, a method is an approach that the *teacher* uses, a strategy or style of instruction, so to speak. Of course, the textbook can suggest a certain kind of methodology. How-ever, the practical restrictions related to cost of production, size of book, and the inflexibility of the printed page do not favor the text-book as the major determiner of instructional methods. We will have more to say on this matter in the next section when we deal with the ways in which teachers can appropriately use textbooks and other materials.

Other factors of lesser importance, as the poll mentioned earlier indicates, are the tokens of modernity, the use of catchwords such as modern, discovery, patterns, structure, and the like. These words tell little about the philosophy and content of the book in themselves. One must look carefully inside the covers to determine the form such im-plied emphasis actually takes.

Consideration of the learner, which the decision-making diagram, Figure 4-1, shows contributing to textbook selection decisions, is a factor but probably not a major one in deciding between most popular texts in use today. On the whole, the formats of books have been made very appealing to children, the vocabulary employed is usually well adjusted to the level of most children, and reasonable provisions are made for both the slower and faster learners, though, at best, this responsibility must rest primarily with the teacher.

Consideration of the teacher's skills and knowledge plays a more important role in textbook choice. Many teachers feel the need to improve their professional competence by increasing their knowledge of mathematics content. However, the amount of time that can be dedicated to such exclusive study is usually limited. One possible solu-tion to this problem is to learn more about content in the very process of teaching.

Studies in the past have suggested that teachers have not grown in their understanding of the subject matter of arithmetic as a result of experience in teaching.[5] Possibly as a result of such studies, greater efforts were made by publishers to assist the teachers. As Weaver reported in 1961,

> Elementary-school mathematics textbooks, workbooks, and work-texts have changed significantly in most instances during the past 25 years. Much more significant changes have occurred in a much shorter time, however, in regard to the Teacher's Manual or Teacher's Guide or Teacher's Edition of the pupils' textbook or worktext. These

---

[5]V. J. Glennon, "Guidance Report of the Commission on Postwar Plans," *The Mathematics Teacher*, November, 1947, 324-25.

publications for the teacher have grown from simple "answer books" to truly professional books on the teaching and learning of mathematics at their respective grade levels. . . . These teacher's editions serve to give her extensive background, suggestion, and guidance in implementing virtually all phases of her program of mathematics instruction.[6]

Thus the potential of the guide to assist the teacher in improving his own grasp of content as well as to conserve his time through helpful suggestions for teaching the material and treating special learning problems becomes an important consideration in the selection of the textbook.

But perhaps the most crucial characteristic that a series must have relates to its central role as the embodiment of the scope and sequence of the curriculum. In regard to this important aspect of the textbook, one must be certain that the development of mathematical ideas, especially ideas newer to the curriculum, is both consistent and persistent.

Former considerations concerning the discipline, drill, and "tool" aspects of mathematics, as well as its social value, have given place to a primary concern with developing a familiarity with important unifying concepts of mathematics. While this new emphasis is compatible with learning the basic skills and with learning to apply them to significant social problems, the need is greater now than ever before to provide for steady, systematic growth of mathematical *ideas* in the child's mind.

The most popular system at present for providing such growth is embodied in the technique of the spiral curriculum. Rather than expecting the child to achieve, in a rather final sense, mastery of some block of material by a given age, or compelling him to begin some particular development at a given time, the spiral curriculum provides him the opportunity to grow through repeated contact with important ideas. At each return to a given structure, an opportunity is provided to increase the depth and breadth of the learner's grasp of that structure in keeping with his abilities, needs, and interests at the time.

The more traditional parts of the curriculum usually afford this spiral approach. However, it is not difficult to find cases where some of the newer topics are met repeatedly without significant development.

The notion of sets is a common case in point. Sets may be mentioned frequently in grades K-2 in connection with whole number ideas but

---

[6]J. F. Weaver in M. V. DeVault, ed., *Improving Mathematics Programs* (Columbus, Ohio: Charles E. Merrill Books, Inc., 1961), p. 401.

with little development of set concepts themselves. The frequency of use of set notions often drops in grades 3 and 4. Then suddenly in grade 5 or 6, set theory itself may receive very heavy emphasis in connection with certain topics from number theory such as Least Common Multiple, Greatest Common Factor, prime factorization, and other ideas which are, among other things, fundamental to developing manipulative skills with fractions. Often this emphasis occurs without adequate preparation of the child's readiness to cope with the rapid new developments. Similar remarks may hold in regard to the consistent and persistent development of the structural properties of operations—commutativity, associativity, and distributivity.

Thus care must be exercised to select texts which not only contain the desired content but also provide a steady, systematic development of ideas in a spiral fashion and which give due regard to *preparation* of the child to abstract, to reason logically, to go back to fundamentals —as he increasingly should know how to do in approaching and performing the work in the higher grades. In particular, the structural properties must be developed beyond the scope of their narrow application to computational processes. A failure to provide this evenly paced development is the source of many learning problems for pupils as they attempt the transition from ESM to secondary level mathematics.

One technique for taking into account so many considerations of varying importance when selecting a textbook is to use a checklist. While no one checklist necessarily serves as an ultimate form by which textbook selection can be made, it may be helpful for the reader to consider the more recent one shown in Figure 4-3 in its entirety. Figure 4-4 is a reproduction of this checklist, designed for use as a guide to teachers by the State Department for Public Instruction in Wisconsin. Some of the points which we have emphasized as key criteria are clearly evident in Sections 1 and 2, sections which actually make up the bulk of the checklist. Sections 3, 4, and 5 retain some of the criteria that have been a part of most similar lists in the past. It would be a useful exercise for the reader to devise a checklist which reflects the structures he would stress in a desirable ESM program and then use the list to rate two or more of the contemporary popular textbook series. This exercise is valuable both with respect to gaining a feel for the magnitude of the task and for the use of such "guidelines" as those given above for sources of suggestions (rather than inflexible rules) for the teacher to use in exercising his own initiative.

Figure 4-4

Sample Criteria Checklist[7]

1. *Philosophy of Program*

   The Program

   (a) Is consistent with the K-12 mathematics program of the school.
   (b) Contains good mathematical development.
   (c) Presents a continuous development of concepts and skills.
   (d) Is teachable and appropriate for the particular level.
   (e) Uses a spiral development.
   (f) Develops concepts through numerous examples.
   (g) Uses consistent and understandable mathematical language.

2. *Key Mathematical Content and Behavioral Objectives of Program*

   A. Arithmetic Concepts

   (a) The program provides for an understanding of sets and numbers, including:

   Cardinal numbers.
   Ordinal numbers.
   Whole numbers (positive integers).
   Fractions (positive rational numbers).
   Negative integers.

   (b) The program provides for an understanding of numeration systems through:

   A variety of grouping activities.
   An emphasis on place values (base 10).
   An introduction to other numeration systems.

   (c) The program provides for an understanding of the concept of order through:

   Experiences in determining "greater than," "less than," and "equals."
   The use of the symbols $<$, $>$, $=$.
   The ordering of a set of numbers (from smallest to largest).

   (d) The program provides for an understanding of number systems, operations and their properties through:

   Experiences with addition (and subtraction as its inverse).
   Experiences with multiplication (and division as its inverse).

---

[7]*K-6 Guidelines to Mathematics,* Wisconsin Department of Public Instruction (Madison, Wis.: The Department, 1967).

Experiences with the structure of the system of whole numbers.
Experiences with the structure of the rational number system.

(e) The program provides for an understanding of the concepts of ratio and proportion through:

Separate treatment of the concept of ratio from that of rational number.
Many experiences entailing the use of ratio and proportion in problem solving.

(f) The program provides for an understanding of computation through:

A developmental program in basic facts.
Experiences developing proficiency in common computation procedures (algorithms).
The use of nondrill activities to build computational skills.

B. Mathematical Sentences

(g) The program provides for an understanding of mathematical sentences through:

Equations and inequalities developed as "translations" and "interpretations" of physical situations.
Intuitive methods suggested for the solution of equations and inequalities.
Practice in the solution of equations and inequalities.
Use of equations and inequalities to solve problems.

C. Geometry Concepts

The program provides for an understanding of the concepts of:

(h) Size and shape through:

Experiences in identifying plane and solid figures.

(i) Sets of points through:

Manipulative and conceptual experiences with points, lines, and planes.

(j) Symmetry through:

The development of symmetry concepts.

(k) Congruence through:

The development of congruence concepts.

(l) Similarity through:

The development of similarity concepts.

(m) Coordinate systems and graphs through:

The use of number line activities and the development of coordinate systems and graphing.

(n) Construction through:

Construction problems.

(o) Measurement through:

Experiences with money and time.
The development of concepts of basic units for length, area, volume, angles.
The development of approximate measures.
Experiences with equivalent measures (and the reduction of measures).
The development of area formulas for squares, rectangles, parallelograms, and triangles.
The development of the linear metric system.

D. Problem Solving

(p) The program provides for an understanding of problem solving through:

Continuous emphasis on problem solving.
Practical help for solving problems.
A wide distribution and variety of problem solving practice.

3. *Methodology Used in and Suggested for Program*

The program provides:
(a) Mathematical concepts correctly and consistently used in explanations.
(b) A variety of approaches in developing a topic.
(c) A basic skills development and maintenance program.
(d) Adequate material for written assignments.
(e) Sufficient material for oral exercises.
(f) An emphasis on estimation and "trial-and-error" techniques in problem solving.
(g) "Mental arithmetic" activities.
(h) Independent thinking activities.
(i) Exercises graduated in difficulty.
(j) Consideration of individual differences.
(k) Clarity of examples.
(l) Supplementary activities for high achievers.
(m) Supplementary-remedial activities for low achievers.
(n) Independent work in geometry or other topics.

4. *Supplementary Aids to Program*

(a) The teacher's manual
Contains mathematical background for content of program.
Provides adequate suggestions.
Suggests numerous activities for enrichment (high and low).
(b) A suggested testing program for use in pupil evaluation is available.
(c) The publishing company provides consultants, films, or other means of inservice aids.

5. *Physical Format of Book*

(a) The general format of the book is attractive to the pupil.
(b) The binding of the book is of good quality.

Topics for Further Investigation

1. Consult a textbook designed for use in a first-year mathematics course for prospective elementary school teachers. What mathematical structures are emphasized? What number universes are developed? What aspect of geometry is stressed? What are the important number and geometric relations treated? Which operations are discussed? How much emphasis is given to problems of symbolization?

2. Select a few structures that you believe are essential for today's ESM curriculum. Construct a checklist that will serve to categorize textbooks according to the degree to which they reflect the structural emphasis you find desirable in a good ESM program. Apply the checklist to two or more series and prepare a sample report, similar to that which a textbook committee might make, rating the two series. What information do you think a final report should contain? (See M. V. DeVault, *Improving Mathematics Programs*, p. 449, for some suggestions.)

3. After examining some of the major textbook series now in use, do you agree or disagree with the claim that they all take into account the child's needs in essentially comparable fashion? If you disagree, what child characteristics do you find must be matched to the textbook? If you agree, evaluate how well the textbooks today meet the child's needs. Consider not just the "average" child but the exceptional child, the member of the minority group, the disadvantaged, and so on. What suggestions would you have to improve textbooks?

4. Investigate the teacher's guides which accompany two or more series. Do you find significant differences between the usefulness to the teachers? Do the guides suggest appropriate methods, materials, and means of evaluation for each lesson or set of lessons? Has some provision been made to help the teacher improve his own content knowledge? Make a checklist and rate the teacher's guides.

5. Investigate several ESM workbooks to determine their respective focus, their quality, and their intended use. Do you find much variation between workbooks in any of these factors?

Bibliography

Bloom, B. S. *Taxonomy of Educational Objectives—Handbook I: Cognitive Domain.* New York: Longmans, Green and Co., 1956.

Bruner, J. H. *The Process of Education.* Cambridge, Mass.: Harvard University Press, 1960.

Fraser, D. M., O. Sand, *et al. Deciding What to Teach.* Project on Instruction, NEA, 1963.

Houston, W. R. (ed.). *Improving Mathematics Education for Elementary School Teachers.* A conference report sponsored by the Science and Mathematics Teaching Center at Michigan State University and the National Science Foundation, 1967.

Krathwohl, D. R. *et al. Taxonomy of Educational Objectives—Handbook II: Affective Domain.* New York: David McKay Company, Inc., 1964.

Lockard, J. D. *Report of the International Clearinghouse on Science and Mathematics Curricular Developments.* Published annually. Available from Science Teaching Center, University of Maryland, College Park, Maryland 20740.

Macdonald, J. B., and J. D. Raths. "Curriculum Research: Problems, Techniques, and Prospects," Chapter 9 in *Review of Educational Research,* Vol. 1(3), June 1963, 322-329.

Mayor, J. R. "Issues and Directions," *The Arithmetic Teacher,* 13(5), May, 1966, 349-54.

National Council of Teachers of Mathematics. *The Growth of Mathematical Ideas, K-12,* 24th Yearbook, 1959.

————. *Topics in Mathematics for Elementary School Teachers.* 29th Yearbook, 1964.

National Education Association. *Guidelines for Textbook Selection.* Report of the Joint Committee of the National Education Association and the American Textbook Publishers Institute. Washington, D.C.: The Association, 1963.

National Science Foundation. *Course and Curriculum Improvement Projects. Mathematics, Science, and Engineering. Elementary School, Secondary School, College, and University.* Superintendent of Documents, U.S. Government Printing Office, Washington, D.C. 10402 (NSF 66-22), September, 1966.

Rising, Gerald R. "Elementary School Mathematics Curriculum Revision—The State of (the) Art," *New York State Mathematics Teachers Journal,* 16(3):90-109, June, 1966.

Wisconsin Department of Public Instruction. *K-6: Guidelines to Mathematics.* Madison, Wis.: The Department, 1967.

5

SYSTEMATIZING ESM
INSTRUCTION

In every art, a perfect control of its technics is a prime requisite of mastership, and one who has complete command of what are termed difficulties by the less skilled, is a virtuoso *(master) in his profession. The study of difficulties . . . is neither so discouraging and wearisome as many suppose, nor so superfluous and needless as many others assert; for only the completest control . . . renders it possible to employ the beauties in style and expression, which . . . appear, to the unobservant or unskilful, to be merely an accumulation of difficulties, but which, under the hands of a true artist, appeal to the sense of the beautiful as successfully as any simple melody, besides lending far greater brilliancy and animation to any artistic rendering.*

Carl Czerny, School of the Virtuoso, *1896*

In the previous chapter we attempted to convey a rationale for decision making which can help systematize ESM curriculum development during this present period of change. The order of decision making has the following sequence. The central mathematical structures to be emphasized in the grades are first determined. Then a textbook series which treats these structures effectively is chosen, subject to the conditions of its having a good teacher's guide and being attractive and readable for the child. This long-range curriculum planning provides the stable but slowly evolving frame of reference in which systematic day-to-day instructional planning can take place and by which long-term development of the program can be guided. The instructional planning involves judicious choice of appropriate methodologies, suitable materials, and effective evaluative techniques from a wide variety of options available. In this vital respect, the teacher focuses all the power of his art and craft on the crucible of learning, the classroom. The successes and failures are observed, learning is tailored to suit the needs of individuals to the extent that present techniques and technology permit, and provisions are made to modify future lessons through immediate observational feedback or by experimental innovative study of difficult problems. The present chapter picks up the flow of decision making at the instructional level.

In Figure 5-1, we see that content decisions and textbook decisions lead through the teacher or instructional team (B) to the decisions that must be made regarding instruction. Thus, the long-range curriculum decisions are made a part of the teachers' objectives and help to give the short-range planning both direction and consistency.

Instruction encompasses four important considerations as indicated in the diagram. These include the selection of *methods* or instructional strategies (3a) for teaching; the selection and use of relevant *materials* (3b); organization of the classroom to provide effective learning experiences (3c); and the evaluation (C) of both the learners' performance and the instructional methods, materials, and organization used in a given lesson.

Also important to instructional decision making is the set of learner characteristics (3d) which the teacher must consider both in group instruction and when adjusting the program particularly to individual needs. These characteristics, or parameters as we may refer to them, include the learners' readiness for the lesson, his attitude, interest, and needs, his reading level, attention span, general intelligence, and so on. These attributes of the child generally fall into three categories: the cognitive or intellectual characteristics, the affective or emotional characteristics, and the psychomotor or muscular coordination characteristics. Inasmuch as these characteristics vary greatly between individuals, the matter of adjusting instruction to the particular learner characteristics of a given class requires that the teacher first know his pupils and, second, be familiar with the variety of techniques that have been found to fit certain of these characteristics.

Looking at the overall picture, we see that instruction basically involves planning, teaching, assigning, diagnosing, and prescribing. The effective teacher understands the nature of each of these tasks and has at his disposal a variety of procedures to deal with each of them. In the past, the method theorist typically advocated teaching techniques

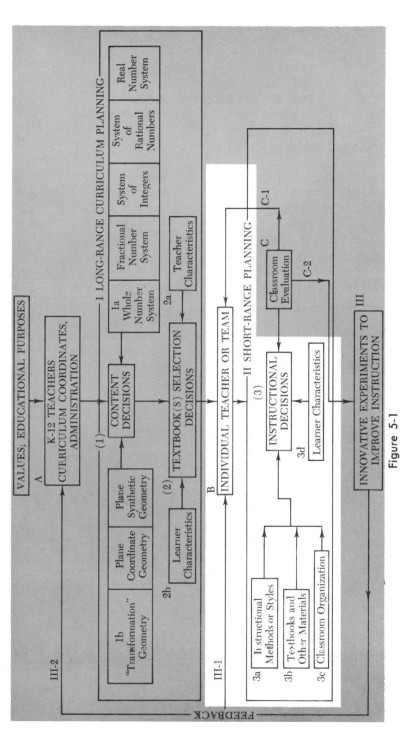

Figure 5-1

An ESM Curriculum Decision Model

which emphasized a given method having a specified number of steps to be followed in the presentation of each lesson. Modern theory, however, provides for greater variety of procedures from which a teacher might choose. This less specific but more powerful approach is based on the belief that a given procedure will be more desirable for particular pupils at particular times than other procedures. The new, more flexible approach also places greater confidence in the teacher's ability to assume the responsibility for the selection of the appropriate procedure at any given time. In the past, fixed recommendations slighted the importance of variable classroom conditions and under-estimated the professional competence and responsibility of teachers.

PLANNING FOR INSTRUCTION

Effective teaching is dependent to a large extent upon the quality of planning which precedes the face-to-face confrontation between teacher and pupils. However, what constitutes good planning is not the same for all teachers, teams, or situations. An interesting research undertaken recently has raised some questions about the extent to which decisions made in formal planning sessions are actually implemented in class-room teaching. Briefly, it suggested that planning is all too often poorly correlated to eventual classroom practice. Two reasons seemed to underlie this fact. On the one hand, it appeared that some teachers are very good at sensing the immediate needs of their pupils and are likely, therefore, to alter plans to meet the demands of the situation as it develops in the classroom. On the other hand, the best of planning often turned out to be ineffective in the hands of the insecure teacher. Uncertainty and insecurity combined to make the planning, in this case, a kind of dreaming which was not actualized in the classroom. This research suggests that, first of all, planning must be realistic in terms of the teacher's understanding of his own role, personality, and fluency with the mathematics content as well as with the capabilities of the pupils.

The teacher must have clearly in mind what he wishes his students to accomplish in mathematics. This preparation can be accomplished only if the teacher understands the mathematics program throughout the elementary school, regardless of the grade level at which he teaches. And, of course, he must have well in mind the goals for his pupils for the year they are under his instruction. Only in the context of clear goals can effective planning for a unit or a single lesson be undertaken. As a second principle of good planning, then, we say that planning must include a clear knowledge of both long-range and immediate goals.

Many teachers experienced with the atomistic approach of traditional mathematics instruction have recognized, or at least thought they recognized, as many goals as there are individual lessons. Some approaches to instruction currently being developed are of a similar type. Programs such as that developed for the individualization of instruction by the Research and Development Center at the University of Pittsburgh include an extensive set of behavioral objectives around which individual lessons are designed. In this sense, each lesson has a specific, separate, and identifiable goal.

While the atomistic approach can well serve special methods, such as programmed instruction, it is difficult for a teacher to remember and implement hundreds of specific goals. Therefore, in most mathematics programs the distinct tendency is to identify the "big ideas" toward which instruction over more than a single class period may be directed.

At any given grade level relatively few of these big ideas are to be taught. A great deal of encouragement can be given to the exploration of ideas beyond or outside of the specifics in the "textbook" program.

As an example, let us consider some of the big ideas which illustrate a possible set of basic ingredients of a third-grade program.

1. Extending ideas of addition and subtraction to include regrouping.
2. Introducing and developing ideas relating to multiplication and division.
3. Developing structural properties of the operations.
4. Developing simple fraction ideas.
5. Extending understandings of the order of numbers to include the rational numbers.
6. Extending ideas of operations of sets.
7. Developing some ideas of logic.
8. Extending ideas of measurement to include some standard measures and reporting of measurements in graph form.
9. Understanding intuitively aspects of geometry to include points, lines, planes, and the union and intersection.
10. Extending concepts of numeration.

These goals are not isolated or discrete but are interrelated in ways which can easily be remembered and implemented by the classroom teacher. For instance, the order in which the big ideas are given here indicates a possible segment of a "spiral" sequence according to which the teacher might wish to take up the topics. Described in terms of the basic sequence given in Figure 4-2, topic 4 introduces a new universe; topics 1 and 10 deal primarily with symbolization and its uses, that is, the development of counting and computing systems; topic 5 deals with the order relations for fractions primarily; topics 2, 3, and 6 fall in the category of understanding operations and their properties; topic 7 might deal with a new universe of ideas such as true and false statements; topic 8 goes outside the realm of pure mathematics to traditional concerns with standard units of measurement, techniques of measuring, and the pictorial representation of results; finally, topic 9 introduces yet another universe of geometric ideas and two operations on sets of these ideas.

Long-range planning should include provisions both to build on big ideas in the learner's earlier experiences and to ready him for work in later grades. Short-term planning, either for a unit or for a single lesson, is designed to provide particular learning experiences relevant to the achievement of one or more of these larger goals.

A third essential ingredient to effective planning is the determination of the instructional method to be employed in the lesson. Are the goals for today's lesson best met through a developmental procedure, a discovery approach, or a deductive method? The teacher who is prepared to plan and implement any one of a variety of instructional methods is in a position to select that approach which seems most appropriate in terms of the specific task of the day.

Many teachers in our schools have failed to give adequate thought to the matter of teaching style and are often actually unaware of the nature of their particular method of instruction. The research work of Flanders[1] and of Gage[2] as well as others has provided striking evidence of the extent to which teachers fail to appreciate the kind of communication patterns they initiate in the classroom. Only when a teacher understands the available alternatives, appreciates the unique values of each alternative, and is able to implement the alternatives can he enrich the instructional program through thoughtful planning. The function of a good teacher's guide is to suggest alternatives to the teacher in accordance with the specific topic under consideration.

Planning also includes the determination of the instructional materials which will be used and the role these materials will play. These

---

[1]N. A. Flanders, "Intent, Action, Feedback: A Preparation for Teaching," *Journal of Teacher Education,* Vol. 14, September, 1963, pp.

[2]N. L. Gage, "A Method for Improving Teacher Behavior," *Journal of Teacher Education,* Vol. 14, September, 1963, pp. 261-66.

decisions go hand-in-hand with those related to instructional method and cannot be made independently. For instance, whether or not the textbook is to be used, when during the presentation of the lesson its use might be most effective, and for which students its use might be most essential may all be important elements in the planning of a given lesson.

Teachers are also giving increasing attention in planning to individual differences. In order to adjust instruction to individual needs, planning must include decisions concerning the extent to which remarks will be directed to all children, the extent to which individual assignments will be made, the extent to which instructional materials will be made available to some children while not necessarily to others, and the extent to which evaluation of the lesson will be differentiated with respect to individual children.

No planning can be considered complete which does not realistically appraise the pupils to be taught. Any such appraisal reveals extensive individual differences in every class. The teacher's task during planning is to take into account the importance of these differences to the attainment of the goals which have been established.

Finally, planning must be designed to include an evaluation of the learning which has taken place. What measurements will be made and what values will be assigned to these measurements? Will these be differentiated according to the pupil's individual learning potential? To what extent will these evaluative means reflect on the quality of instruction? At the same time individual learning is evaluated, what implications can be made for the improvement of the teacher's instructional efforts for another day? The details of evaluation will be treated more fully in Chapter 6.

Specific details concerning the manner in which teachers go about their planning tasks will vary considerably. In some schools and for some individual teachers, a planning book, which to a large extent formalizes the planning procedures, seems to be effective. Other teachers are able to plan informally and still include consideration of the essential elements. Usually beginning teachers may be expected to profit more from extensive and formal planning procedures than will more experienced teachers. Many experienced teachers say they plan even though they sometimes put few thoughts on paper. Many supervisors have observed, however, that those teachers who are reputedly master teachers usually are those who have in their own way formalized planning procedure which results in written lesson plans that give consideration to the essential elements we have discussed. The best planning, however, is no substitute for teaching expertise in the classroom. It is likewise true that teaching expertise is likely to be most effective when it evolves from careful planning.

TEACHING

Perhaps the most important single influence on the quality of the learner's mathematical experience in the classroom is the teaching act itself. The mathematical content, the instructional materials, the personality of the teacher, the previous experiences of the learners are all secondary in importance to the central activity of the teacher in direct teacher-pupil interaction. This being so, surprisingly little attention is given to this essential ingredient. True, many factors influence the quality and nature of the teaching act. The teacher's understanding of mathematics and his security in the mathematics classroom are as important contributors in determining the nature of his teaching behavior as is his understanding of learners and of the learning process. But let us assume for the moment that an adequate minimum mathematics knowledge and knowledge about the learner and learning has been attained and turn our attention to the discussion of teaching styles or methods.

Teaching Styles

A great deal of writing and research has been directed toward the identification of effective teaching styles or methods. The venerable Socratic method; the specific styles developed in the nineteenth century such as the Herbartian, Pestalozzian, and Froebelian methods; the early twentieth-century methods advocated in the writing of Dewey; and the widely used expository or lecture method are all antecedents to concerns which direct current research on teaching style.

Two broad areas of approach seem to dominate the research in this field. First are those studies related to interaction analysis in which the verbal behavior of the teacher is analyzed. The moment-to-moment teacher comments are the concern of these researchers.

Teachers, through these studies, have been identified, for example, as dominative or integrative (Anderson and Brewer),[3] as direct or indirect (Flanders),[4] and as content oriented or person oriented (May

---

[3] H. H. Anderson and J. E. Brewer, "Studies of Teachers' Classroom Personalities. II Effects of Teachers' Dominative and Integrative Contacts on Children's Classroom Behavior," *Applied Psychology Monographs,* No. 8, 1946.

[4] N. A. Flanders, "Teacher Influence, Pupil Attitudes, and Achievement," *Cooperative Research.*

and DeVault).[5] Few of these studies have been directed specifically toward mathematics, but each represents one way of helping teachers better understand themselves as communicators with students.

These researchers tend to be atomistic in their approach to the analysis of teaching styles; such research appears to be less useful for our present purposes than the second kind of analyses which encompass the totality of an instructional lesson through which a teacher guides the learner to a particular understanding or understandings related to the goals of the lesson. Teaching styles to which we wish to give special attention include inductive, deductive, and discovery methods. Although clear-cut distinctions among these methods are not easy to make, the classroom teacher needs to understand the elements of each, the advantages and disadvantages of each, and when to utilize each in his own classroom teaching.

Inductive-Deductive Methods

Teaching styles differ not in the content but in the ordering of the content. Ausubel[6] identifies in the deductive method a technique which he calls the *advanced organizer*. The concept or the principle to be learned is stated clearly at the outset and from that statement the teacher moves to an explanation of its meaning and illustrates its use with a number of examples. Only after its use has been demonstrated are the pupils asked to use the principle in a set of examples while the teacher makes himself available to discuss with the learners any particular difficulties they may be having. Finally, a series of practical exercises are provided.

The reverse procedure is usually called the inductive approach. The students are at first presented with a problem situation in which they explore ways in which to solve the problem. A variety of solutions or ways of solving the problem may come from the children; these solutions are shared through discussion without placing a preferential value on one technique as opposed to another. Other situations may be presented to provide children with additional exploratory situations. Following this general exploratory phase, the discussion is directed toward making some tentative conclusion about the principle which has been utilized in the solution of the problem situations. Finally, as in the deductive approach, a series of practice exercises are provided to

---

[5]Frank B. May and M. Vere DeVault, "Hypothetical Dimensions of Teachers' Communication," *American Educational Research Journal*, 4:271-278, May, 1967.
[6]David P. Ausubel, *The Psychology of Meaningful Verbal Learning* (New York: Grune and Stratton, 1963).

confirm and extend the child's view of the context in which the principle is valid. The general outline of the lessons might be similar to that presented in Figure 5-2.

Deductive Approach	*Inductive Approach*
1. Presentation of principle.	1. Presentation of problem situation to be solved through exploration by the pupils.
2. Illustration by the teacher of the use of the principle in the solution of specific examples.	2. Discussion by the class of the various approaches which have been used in the solution of the problem.
3. Assignment of specific examples to be solved by the pupils under the careful supervision of the teacher.	3. Discussion leading to some tentative ideas about patterns, relationships, or generalizations which appear to be operating in the solutions which have been discussed.
4. Discussion led by the teacher designed to clarify any difficulties which appear in the work of the pupils.	4. Application of some of the tentative ideas to specific problems situation to test the validity of the generalization about to be made.
5. Assignment of practice exercises in which the principle is to be utilized.	5. Discussion of results in the testing of tentative generalizations and possibly the verbalization of the principle which has been operating in these situations.
	6. Assignment of practice exercises in which the principle is to be utilized, clarified, and generalized.

Outline for Inductive-Deductive Lessons

Figure 5-2

Examples of the same lesson taught under each of the two methods, inductive and deductive, follow.

A study which is of interest is that by Worthen[7] in which he found that the deductive method was superior when considering immediate results but that the inductive was superior for purposes of retention. Although the teacher variable in both of these studies was controlled

---

[7]Blaine R. Worthen, "A Comparison of Discovery and Expository Sequencing in Elementary Mathematics Instruction," in J. M. Scandura (ed.), *Research in Mathematics Education* (Washington, D.C.: National Council of Teachers of Mathematics, 1967), pp. 44-59.

reasonably well, it can be expected that for some teachers in some situations the deductive method will be superior, whereas for other teachers in other situations the inductive method will prove the desirable one. Teachers should be familiar with each method and should be able to plan and implement lessons using either one and thereby come to some tentative conclusions relative to the times when a given method is most suitable for him.

Figure 5-3

Illustrative Lesson Plans

Illustrative lesson using first the deductive method and then,
for the same lesson, the inductive method

Lesson Objectives: To develop a functional familiarity with the concepts of odd and even numbers.

Behavioral Objectives: The learner should be able to
1. *Identify* any *given* whole number as being either odd or even.
2. *Construct* examples of odd and even numbers in any decade range whatever. [In other words, he should exhibit behavior indicating that he has attained the concept that base ten numerals name even or odd numbers according as the "unit's digit" is even or odd respectively.]
3. *Predict* the parity [odd or even] of the sums and differences of any two whole numbers.
4. Present a rationale for believing that the sets of even and odd numbers are both infinite.
5. Construct the *next* even or odd number after *any* given one.

Assumed Background of the Learner: Previous experience with arranging objects into "two by n" arrays. In cases where the two 1 x n subsets of the array turn out to be equivalent, the learner should respond by describing the number as being "even"; where one subset *necessarily* has an extra element, the learner should describe the number as "odd." Thus the child should have a physical picture to associate with the words *even* and *odd* and should be able to build examples of even and odd numbers with a small set of concrete objects.

Deductive Method: *

1. State purpose: "Today we want to think some more about even numbers and whole numbers." [Take a little time to review past experiences; make sure each child can present an array for small even or odd numbers and can also identify a given array as being representative of either even or odd numbers.]
2. Expand purpose statement to make goal more precise: "We want to go on

---

Note: Teachers' comments are in quotes; typical pupil responses are in parentheses; suggestions to the teacher are in brackets.

one more step now to see if the following facts are always true about the *answer* you get when you add even numbers together [show an example] or add odd numbers together [another example], or add even numbers to odd numbers [final example]." [State concept to be attained explicitly.] "We want to show that the sums will always obey the following rules:

a. even number + even number = even number
b. odd number + odd number = even number
c. even number + odd number = odd number
d. odd number + even number = odd number."

3. "When we draw an array [on the chalkboard] or build one with blocks, we begin by lining up a pair of objects, like this:

x   . . .

x   . . .

so that *one* end is always even. How do you decide whether the number pictured is odd or even?" (At the termination, whether *it* is odd or "even.") [Completes an array.] "Is this one odd or even"? [Change it.] "How about this: even or odd"?

4. "Good. Now, what is the *largest* even number?" [State subpurposes.] "Let's see how to show that there is *no* largest even number. Build an even number of any size you wish with the blocks." [After completion:] "Can you build a larger even number? How?" (Add another pair of blocks.) "Let's play a game. Suppose I build a huge even number like this." [Put down lots of pairs of blocks, more than one would care to count.] "Now I claim that this is the largest even number. Whatever it is, I'm not quite sure. Do you believe me?" (No.) "Well then, show me how to build a larger one." [Pupil builds a larger one.] "Is that the *next* larger one? How do you *always* build the *next* larger even number after *any* given one?" (Put down another pair of blocks.) "Is there, then, any *largest* even number?" (No.) "Why not?" (You can always put down another pair of blocks.)

5. "Now let's look at the same questions, only this time concentrate on *odd* numbers. What is the *largest* odd number?" [How can we show that there is no largest odd number?]

"Build an odd number of any size you wish." [After completion:] "Can you build a larger odd number? How?" (Add another pair of blocks at the "even" end but leave the "odd" end as it was.) "Well, it looks to me then that you make a larger odd number in the same way that you make a larger even number. Is that right? Is there a largest odd number? Here, I'll build a very large odd number and play the same game. I don't know exactly which odd number I have here but I claim that I'm sure that it is certainly the largest that anyone can make. Do you believe me?" (No.) "Then you are going to have to show me a larger one because I won't believe it until I see it." [After 2 blocks are added:] "Is that the *next* odd number? How do you *always* build the *next* larger odd number that follows after *any* given odd number? O.K., good. I think you have that idea now."

6. "But here is a problem. Suppose we take an even number [like this one] and *add* to it another even number [like this one; form the union of the two sets]. What kind of number is the sum?" (*Even*, because you can match the even ends together and the opposite ends of each addend will be even.) "Let's record that in the following table:

+	E	O
E		
O		

'Any even number added to any even number gives us another even number every time,' is what the table says."

"And that suggests another problem: What about adding any odd number to any odd number? Our 'rule' says that this should be *even*. Can you see how that is so?" [Children experiment with their blocks until someone discovers a way of joining the *odd* ends together so that the remaining ends of the array are both even; for those that join the *even* ends, just say that we can't tell much about such a number since in the past we only played with arrays that had *one* end odd. The other end was always even. Try again to get it even on one end and then we'll take a look at the other end to see what kind of number it is.]

7. [Now switch from blocks to cardboard cutouts having the following shapes, but having different specific dimensions or lengths:

Give each learner a supply of each type.] "Which shape represents an even number? An odd number? Do you know which *particular* even (odd) number the shape represents?" (No.)

8. "Now fit two even numbers together. What kind of number is the *sum*? Fit two odd numbers together; what kind of number is the *sum*? Will that always be true for *any* odd number? How shall we record this fact in our table?"

9. "Can you make up a problem where the answer will go in one of the remaining spaces in the table? Solve the problem."

10. "Make up a problem for the fourth space of the table. What is the problem? Show me a solution."

11. "Fine. So, in general, what can we say about sums of *two* even numbers? of two *odd* numbers? of *one* odd number and *one* even number or vice-versa?"

12. [For the quicker students:] "Perhaps you might try to find out what happens when you add together more than two even numbers; or more than two odd numbers; or just a whole bunch of either even or odd numbers. Is it possible to predict the *kind* of result we would get without actually finding the answer to specific problems? In general, what *rule* would you follow to tell if 2 + 547 + 69 + 7,110 + 3,333,333 + 14 comes out even or odd?" [Some practice can then be given to test out particular cases and gain some skill in finding and predicting the parity of sums.]

Inductive Method:

1. Motivate the problem: "We have 7 boys in the room and 9 girls. Suppose we have to go down to the art room as a class. And let's suppose that I have you line up two at a time so that we can go down there quickly and quietly. What I'd like to know is this: would everyone have a partner to

walk with or would there be one person left without a partner?" [Some guesses come from the class, some right and some wrong, very likely.]

2. "Well, we would like to know for sure, so get out some counters to act as boys and girls and let's look at this problem. Do you remember how to show an even number with counters? An odd number? What tells you, when you look at an array, whether the number is even or odd?" [Present

   x x x x x
   subproblem situation.] "What can you tell about this one? x x x x x x x
   Can you rearrange it so that it looks like a 'regular' even number? Good."

   "Now, who can name the *largest* even number?" [Perhaps someone will suggest a candidate.] "It that the largest one?" [Hopefully, a pupil will name a larger one; if not the teacher can suggest that the class test the last named even number $+ 2$ for parity. This interactive questioning, hypothesis, and testing continues until it seems clear that no largest even number exists. In the same way, a similar conclusion is reached concerning the set of odd numbers.]

   [This general development can be handled in such a way that the "infinite" property of the set of even or odd numbers is made heavily dependent on the possibility of building a "next" even or odd number simply by adding *two* to the given number. Examination of a few cases should enable the pupils to induce this general technique for generating the next even or odd number. Finally, sum up the result in a statement of the subgoal:] "Since, in every case, we could build the next larger even or odd number by adding two to the given number, it seems true that there should be no largest even number and no largest odd number. Such a set of numbers that has no end is called an infinite set. What kind of set is the collection of *all* counting numbers?" (Infinite set.)

3. "Now build two sets of even numbers; we'll pretend one is the set of girls and one is the set of boys. Next, form the union of the two sets. What kind of number is the sum, odd or even?" [Ask individual children; give them time to generalize; put some examples on the board selected from the work of several children.] "All right; each of you used *different* particular even numbers but you all got the same *kind* of result: What is the common result?" [Hypothesis: the sum of *any* two even numbers seems to be even; test the hypothesis in a number of cases; then introduce the *table* of results here at the end as in the deductive lesson.]

+	E	O
E		
O		

   "Is there anything else that we can learn about sums of even and odd numbers here?" [Possibly one of the children will suggest forming the sum of two odd numbers; follow it through much as the above example.]

4. [The children are allowed to pursue the development as far as they seem able to comfortably go, generalizing the results as much as possible. The teacher may introduce the geometric figure to represent even and odd as in the deductive lesson, if it seems necessary. Finally, the results are summed

up in table form, and in colloquial language for the time being. Some children may want to look at other operations in a similar way. Some practice can then be given to test out a number of particular cases and gain some skill in finding sums.]

The Discovery Approach

Probably no educational idea has been more widely discussed in recent years than the concept of discovery. The ambiguity with which this discussion proceeds grows out of a lack of agreement on several points. First, confusion seems to exist concerning whether we are talking of discovery teaching, discovery learning, or teaching discovery, the latter meaning to teach the skills of discovery approaches to the investigation of phenomena. Second, confusion arises because so much variety may be found in the programs which purport to teach by discovery. Some of these programs are represented by very carefully controlled pupil experiences which lead to discovery, whereas others are much less controlled and represent a kind of autonomous discovery on the part of the learner. Third, little in the research literature provides useful data or conclusions for those who would develop classroom practices built on discovery techniques.

By and large, it can be said that researchers and teachers are agreed that a teaching approach exists which we might call discovery and that it does have certain characteristics which might be identified. In addition, the fact is generally recognized that such an approach has certain values for improving instructional procedures in the classroom. What are some of the characteristics of discovery teaching and what are the advantages of such an approach?

The most prominent characteristic of discovery teaching is that it is embedded in an inductive teaching approach. Discovery procedures move from a presentation of several specific cases to a generalization about these cases.

In this form of instruction, the child is led to his own formulation or discovery of the essential ideas before he sees or hears a statement which efficiently verbalizes the concept. In this way, some concrete embodiment of the idea has been incorporated into his thinking prior to the time at which he might be tempted to memorize a glib verbalization as a substitute for learning the idea behind it.

Z. P. Dienes,[8] a researcher and teacher who has devoted much effort

---

[8]Zoltan P. Dienes, *Modern Mathematics for Young Children* (New York: Herder and Herder, 1966).

to discovery-oriented instruction and learning, describes the way in which children learn abstract ideas in the following three stages:

1. A preliminary, somewhat groping stage during which situations are handled more or less in the random fashion of a child's playful exploring activity. This can be encouraged to mature by providing . . . purposeful "games," leading eventually to a heightened awareness of the direction in which a new insight is being prepared.
2. Then follows usually an intermediate, more structured stage, during which the rules according to which events take place are realized and "played with." . . . This leads to the eventual *moment of insight*, when the whole pattern seems to fall into place.
3. The achievement of the insight is followed by an almost compulsive desire to *use* the new insight. The more sophisticated way of "using" an insight is to try to examine what it is that has in fact been put together; what exactly have we realized? This is *analysis*. The more usual way is to find situations in which the insight can be used with advantage. This is *practice*.

The success of discovery techniques is heavily dependent upon the learners' freedom to speculate, hypothesize, make errors without embarrassment, learn from the contradictions or inconsistencies such "errors" may produce, and experience the growth of mathematical ideas in a firsthand fashion. The teacher's role in discovery-oriented learning is to provide the kind of atmosphere in which intellectual exploration is encouraged and rewarded.

It is not always easy for teachers to provide such an atmosphere. We have a long tradition to struggle against, for one thing. The still prevalent notion that arithmetic is primarily a tool subject has helped maintain the notion that if the child doesn't get his facts and terminology perfectly straight in grade school, something dreadful will befall him in high school. Thus, in spite of strenuous efforts that have been made to overcome authoritarian, expository type of teaching, the tendency is always to fall back into this mode in order to push the learners along toward some level of proficiency that may have come to be expected by the end of a particular grade level.

The pressures generated by this sort of teacher attitude tend to make the teacher *attack* the errors the learner makes rather than *reward* the part of his thinking which is on the right track. Contrary to expectations, an instructional setting which emphasizes the correction of errors is not likely to prepare the learner well for later mathematics learning. It will, however, probably induce a variety of undesirable feelings including a dislike for mathematics.

On the other hand, the teacher who properly encourages the tentative explorations for mathematical truth by providing opportunity for the child to shape and sharpen his tentative grasp of new ideas will build the confidence needed, as Jerome Bruner phrases it, to enjoy mathe matics and travel far in pursuit of mathematical ideas and skills.

The teacher's attitude is revealed in the questions he uses to guide interaction as well as the response he makes to the pupil's remarks. If the questions are rhetorical in nature or employ such strong cues that the pupil senses that only one possible answer will be acceptable, then the learning is not by discovery of mathematics but rather by discovery of that which satisfies the teacher.

Exposition by the teacher is not ruled out as a suitable method. For example, it is difficult to conceive of the child "discovering" how to write a numeral such as "2." Exposition in the case of certain conventions, agreements, or definitions may be very efficient and satisfactory. In the upper grades, relatively more expository teaching may be necessary than in the primary grades.

Nor do we mean to imply that the teacher must always agree, right or wrong, with a learner's response. If the learner asks the teacher to confirm some hypothesis which happens to be false, it may be most appropriate for the teacher to reply, "I don't think that is true. Why don't you take a look at this possibility?" He may then suggest some activity that will lead the pupil to find a contradiction or inconsistency for himself.

Thus the point is more in the nature of *how* the teacher teaches rather than in simply *what* is done. Many little things add up to shape the classroom atmosphere into one of warmth and respect for the learners' efforts or one predominantly of suspicion, criticism, and blame.

Perhaps another example will help illustrate the kind of learning activity that is most desirable in a modern ESM program. A familiar exercise in many new ESM programs is to create a table of "basic facts" for some operation defined on a particular universe. In the simplest example of such an activity, the child may rely on direct counting to establish his facts. However, if the operation is commutative, a certain symmetrical pattern will gradually develop, much like the picture in a jigsaw puzzle. The children who sense this pattern may utilize it to fill in the remaining spaces rapidly. The other children, sensing that some are finished early, will wonder, not in despair about *what* they are doing, but, out of curiosity, *how* the others are doing it so quickly! In such a situation, every child is assured of at least being able to finish the task but, at the same time, is stimulated to search for more effective means to carry it out.

If an error occurs in filling in some particular fact, it is not made an object of ridicule by other class members but rather the source of common learner error: The inconsistency of the mistaken response is revealed by the fact that it does not fit the symmetrical pattern. From such experiences, the child learns to look for internal consistency among the ideas he works with and to resort to the authority of the mathematics for guidance rather than to the authority of the teacher. One can see in the work of Davis examples of both the *directed* discovery technique as well as an autonomous, learning-teaching procedure. His written materials[9] are representative particularly of a very carefully sequenced set of questions designed to control and direct the discovery experience of the learner. On the other hand, his films[10] are representative of both techniques in that the main idea is pursued through a carefully controlled sequence of questions, while at the same time Davis is quick to accept and explore the peripheral statements and findings of learners which represent by-products in the planned lesson. These latter are more representative of autonomous discovery experiences.

Teaching children *how to* discover may be at the same time one of the most useful and the most difficult tasks a teacher may undertake. Ample evidence seems to indicate that learning set has an important influence on behavior. Many discovery-oriented programs of instruction require that the learner be provided at an early stage those experiences which will first provide an expectation that *his* initiative will determine to a large extent what learning takes place and a *positive* expectation that fruitful learning experience will result from his own efforts in seeking out relationships and meanings among the various elements of the experience. Secondly, once this expectation is built, skills requisite to this kind of learning must be developed. Children are not naturally embued with a full-fashioned kit of discovery skills—or are they? It would seem that the infant and preschool child is oftentimes, indeed,

---

[9] R. B. Davis, *Matrices, Functions, and Other Topics: Student Discussion Guide* (The Madison Project, 1963); *Discovery in Mathematics: Student Discussion Guide* (Reading, Mass.: Addison-Wesley Publishing Co., Inc., 1964); *Discovery in Mathematics: A Text for Teachers* (Reading, Mass.: Addison-Wesley Publishing Co., Inc., 1964); *Matrices, Logic, and Other Topics: Student Discussion Guide* (The Madison Project, 1966); D. D. Machtinger, *Experimental Course Report/ Kindergarten (Report #2, July 1965)* (The Madison Project).

[10] *Notes on the Film: A Lesson with Second Graders* (booklet to accompany film of the same name.) (The Madison Project, 1962).

an automatic explorer and discoverer. He discovers his hands, his toes, various aspects of his immediate environment and then moves to the exploration of a wider world which is his as a 3-year-old. Many believe the rigidly controlled early school environment tells the child that exploration, or discovery, is not appreciated and is, indeed, discouraged here. Research has indicated that a very large percentage of the questions (one element of exploratory behavior) in the classroom at the early primary levels are asked by *pupils* but, by the intermediate grades, pupils docilely respond to the largest percentage of questions asked by *teachers*. Essentially the school experience is not a discovery experience in such cases. If it is intended to be, then very specific steps must be taken to make it so. Much of this effort, obviously must be directed to the rechannelling of teacher behavior, but much of it also must follow in redirecting both the expectations and the behavior of learners.

Learners in discovery-oriented situations must be encouraged to ask questions, to seek relationships and patterns among the various concepts and stimuli they face, to set tentative hypotheses about these relationships, to test these hypotheses, to make generalizations, to discuss with others their hunches and expectations, and to differ from others in both the manner in which they explore and in the results of their explorations. All of these elements of discovery do not come automatically but come as the result of proper and thoughtful encouragement over a relatively long period of time. Classroom teachers have been known to "try" discovery teaching and after a lesson or a brief series of lessons to report that such procedures are ineffective. Even if the teacher had very carefully prepared himself for this teaching, a failure to anticipate the discovery abilities of the learners might doom the lesson to failure at the outset.

The reader should recognize that research has verified little relative to discovery experiences in the classroom. Authorities in the field of mathematics curriculum, although not in complete agreement on any extended series of ideas relating to discovery learning-teaching, generally agree that discovery activities do have value in the elementary school mathematics curriculum. Writers and researchers have differed in their approach to the study of this problem and individual teachers will differ too. What is important, it would seem, is that teachers recognize the utility of discovery approaches as an individual matter. How a given teacher approaches discovery activities and how he encourages learning set for discovery will depend upon a great many factors which are a part of his background experience and his perceptions of his effectiveness as he works with pupils in his class.

An Eclectic Position

In spite of the fact that several distinctly different teaching styles can be identified, there is no basis for assuming that one particular teaching style is always appropriate. The teacher is bombarded constantly with perceptions of himself, his class, and individual learners in that class. His choice of teaching style should be altered as these perceptions change. For some content, for instance definition of terms, a deductive approach would seem to be most appropriate; for other content, such as set intersection and set union, inductive or discovery approaches may be appropriate. The master teacher is that teacher who alters his teaching style to meet his perceptions of a particular learning situation.

Making Assignments

Assigned work undertaken by pupils will be considered in four parts as identified in Figure 5-4. The purpose of the assignment and the independence with which the assignment is to be undertaken are critical dimensions of any attempt to identify assignment of tasks to be undertaken by the pupils.

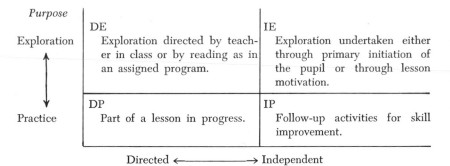

Purpose		
Exploration	DE Exploration directed by teacher in class or by reading as in an assigned program.	IE Exploration undertaken either through primary initiation of the pupil or through lesson motivation.
Practice	DP Part of a lesson in progress.	IP Follow-up activities for skill improvement.

Directed ⟵——————⟶ Independent

Classification System for Assignment Activities

Figure 5-4

The four types of assignments are not meant to be as discrete as the diagram would seem to suggest in Figure 5-4. Rather the expectation is that practice assignments, for instance, range from those which are a part of a lesson in progress and in which the learner makes little independent effort, to those which are follow-up activities undertaken largely through independent efforts of the learner. A middle position, for example, might be illustrated by a lesson-in-progress assignment in which the teacher differentiates the assignments in such a way that he spends considerable time with a few pupils while most of the class is working quite independently. Likewise, on the continuum of the other dimension of the design, certain exploratory or discovery skills might consist of either practice under the direct guidance of the teacher during a classroom lesson or exploration which the learner's interests may suggest independently of the teacher's expectations.

Directed Practice

Many mathematics classes utilize directed practice activities as a part of the procedure of a developing lesson. As an example, we might consider a lesson in which a teacher has presented a problem situation involving regrouping in subtraction. After some time is spent in exploring this particular idea and sharing among pupils in the class the various approaches different children have taken in the solution of this problem, the teacher may assign an additional three problems for each to work. As work proceeds, the teacher moves about the class helping where help is needed, observing the work of individual children in an attempt to better understand their readiness for work in this and following areas. Seldom is a lesson complete without some attempt on the part of the teacher to determine the extent to which pupils have understood the ideas presented in the lesson. Certainly this kind of directed practice is essential before children move to more independent practice activities.

Independent Practice

End-of-class, or homework, assignments are a part of the independent practice identified in Figure 5-2. Perhaps few mistakes are made more frequently by teachers than that of sending home assignments which the pupil is not ready to do in an independent fashion. The assumption often seems to be that, as a simple consequence of the fact that some topic has been taught in the classroom, the pupils understand the topic and are ready to undertake its further development through independent practice. The cartoons which depict fathers struggling with Junior's homework grow out of either erroneous concepts of what homework assignments should be or out of errors in judgment on the part of the teacher concerning the readiness of the pupils for the assignment which is made.

Directed Exploration

Specific questions can be raised to evoke exploration on the part of the pupils. If the set of natural numbers is closed for addition, is the set of primes closed for addition? Or children may turn to a text including programed materials for exploration directed toward the better understanding of certain geometric concepts. In a classroom in which there is a great variety of materials available, children may be expected to explore in a variety of ways and yet in a rather restricted or directed sense.

Independent Exploration

Assignments which encourage rather wide-ranging activities of exploration in mathematics are oftentimes fruitful in long-range terms. An exploratory mission which sends the early second grader home with a blank chart in which he is attempting to build a multiplication table is real exploration for that child. With aids such as Cuisenaire rods, he has the facility to work with great independence in the exploration of his idea. Such an idea or question might have been posed appropriately by the teacher or might have been raised initially by the child. Another example of independent exploration would be the intermediate grade child who begins to sense the role of function in describing the many relationships in our everyday world and starts a notebook in which he has a great variety of examples drawn from his out-of-class activities, from newspaper reports, and from reference materials.

Assignments Summarized

The most effective mathematics program might be expected to be the one which amply and appropriately utilizes all four types of assignments. Ample attention should be given to practice activities, both directed and independent, but just as important are the exploratory activities which likewise can be undertaken as part of the mathematics lesson itself and as part of the extended mathematics activities of the learner.

Use of the Textbook and Other Materials

Appropriate Use of Textbooks

The most commonly used instructional materials in mathematics classrooms are the textbooks. Both advantages and disadvantages accrue from the widespread and sometimes exclusive use of the textbook. The textbook, as we have indicated, does provide the authoritative content and sequence for a mathematics program. As a result, some teachers use the text as the *determiner* of the curriculum in their class. Others see the textbook as providing the content and sequence, but they use it only as the *outline and guide* for their own efforts and as a source of supplementary information or exercises. For still others the textbook has a lesser place and the program is derived from other sources, possibly a televised program or from programed materials.

Which of these three approaches is utilized in a given classroom should be determined at least in part by the mathematical and instructional understanding of the classroom teacher. Increasingly, teacher education programs, both inservice and preservice, are designed to provide teachers with much more mathematics content than was the case only a very few years ago. As a result, this improvement is causing a gradual shifting of the nature of mathematics curriculum in our classrooms and in the use of textbooks. From the teacher who feels relatively insecure in the area of mathematics instruction, one might expect a somewhat heavier reliance on the textbook. As experience and mathematical knowledge of the teacher increases, reliance on the text or other external sources can be safely reduced to permit the teacher greater control over the scope and sequence of activities.

Of special assistance in promoting the teacher's competence is the teacher's guide. Over the past 25 to 30 years, the nature of the teacher's guide has changed from a kind of answer book to a rich resource of pedagogical and mathematical information. One of its most important features, yet one that seems almost too obvious to mention, is the simple matter of the statement of purpose of the lesson. All too frequently one observes teachers using textbooks without appreciating the purpose or purposes for which the pages were designed. The teacher's guide or manual also includes suggested instructional styles for presenting the lesson. Although few teachers will find the suggestions precisely appropriate for their classes, they do provide ideas from which teachers can develop their own lessons in a way which is appropriate to the objectives and presentation of the pupil text. As teachers become increasingly familiar with a given text series, they may be expected to find themselves comfortable and able to move away from excessive dependence on the text and the teacher's guide.

For most teachers the textbook will serve as only one of many instructional materials. The textbook used most effectively serves as a resource for *learners*. But the classroom procedure is designed in such a way that the center of the instructional effort is the teacher, not the text. The *teacher* understands mathematics, instruction, and learners in a way which makes it possible for him to organize resources for effective instruction. For such a teacher, the mathematics lessons seldom begins with the textbook. Rather it begins with the establishment of a mathematical situation or problem about which a discussion is centered.

Consider as an example early third graders who have not had formal instruction involving regrouping in addition or subtraction. The teacher may begin with a presentation of seemingly familiar addition exercises in the following order:

$$\begin{array}{cccc} 34 & 62 & 27 & 48 \\ +25 & +33 & +36 & +18 \\ \hline \end{array}$$

The children are asked to work these exercises and to note any ways in which the first two differ from the second two. Some of the children, as they work the latter two, use aids such as sticks or markers grouped by ones and tens in finding the sum. After most have completed their work or at least have had an opportunity to explore the exercises, the teacher selects the work of four or five children to be placed on the board. He selects the four or five most diverse approaches—not the ones most nearly like that in the text; not the ones which might be thought of as most mature, but those which in the teacher's judgment will provide the most interesting and challenging sources of discussion. After discussing the several approaches to the solution of the problem, two or three additional exercises are given and children are told to work them in whatever way they wish. This assignment provides the teacher with an opportunity to move about the room watching children as they work. He senses the extent to which they understand the discussion concerning each of the approaches presented. If a child moves to a more mature approach which was discussed but one he had not used initially, some indication is provided of his understanding of what had been discussed. On the other hand, if a child continues to use markers to solve the problem, the teacher will likely recognize this as an indication that for that particular child, some basic understandings related to regrouping are still to be developed. When the teacher feels that enough of the children do understand the nature of regrouping and its role in this kind of exercise, he then asks the pupils to turn to the textbook and compare their own work with the approach suggested in the text.

No coercion is needed to force the text's method on the class *en masse*. If some youngster needs to use counters or fingers as a crutch to calculation, so be it. (Curiously, teachers who object to crutches in addition and subtraction will *themselves* use crutches in multiplication and division without giving it a second thought. For instance, try writing the product of 42 × 29 without using the traditional "partial products" crutch; or write down directly the quotient 983 ÷ 37 without using the "partial quotients" or "partial remainders" crutch.)

Another way in which a text may be used is simply as a source of practice exercises. During the time pupils are practicing with the exercises in the book the teacher moves about the room noting their particular strengths and needs, giving encouragement and help as needed.

Throughout classroom discussions which can oftentimes occupy an entire lesson without turning to the text, questions will arise related to certain rules, procedures, statements of properties, and so on. Here again the teacher may wish to turn to the text for clarification and assistance.

A third kind of approach makes practically no use of a text as such. In this instance, other kinds of materials or the teacher himself become the source of content, demonstrator of skills, and sequence. It is not recommended that many beginning teachers start their instructional programs from this point of view. Implied in such an approach is a thorough understanding of mathematics, of instruction (including textbook materials), and of learners. This understanding may come with experience, but the most effective mathematics instruction of this type is to be found in these classes where teachers have strong mathematics preparation, understand curriculum building in elementary education, have much support from other faculty members and their administration, and are able to teach independently of any single source of program with facility, security, and effectiveness. Many teachers might well dedicate their long-term professional efforts toward this kind of instruction.

Workbooks

One of the most controversial issues in mathematics education is the role of the workbook. Most text series are accompanied by workbook materials, particularly in grades 3 through 6. The textbooks for the first two grades are typically soft-back books and resemble workbooks in format. In use, however, they are the textbooks.

Workbooks available today are of two kinds: practice and enrichment. They are best used when they are used to provide ways of meeting individual differences. Seldom does an entire class need additional practice beyond that for which materials are provided in the text on a given computation skill. Rather, the need is for something which at just the right time can be made available to that child who has difficulty with the work which most of the class seems to have mastered. The workbook can be effectively used.

At the other end of the continuum is the child who is able to work independently and has a superior grasp of much of the material which the class has been studying. In such cases the enrichment workbook can be of much value.

Multi-sensory Materials

Mathematics is many things to many people, but in the elementary school one of the most important ideas about mathematics is its relation to the physical world. Mathematics finds an important application in describing the quantitative and spacial aspects of our environment. This very fundamental understanding is oftentimes entirely missed by children in our classes. This lack of understanding may grow out of either the failure to relate the symbolic aspects of mathematics to the real world or inappropriate and inadequate attempts to show this relationship. Multi-sensory materials afford an excellent opportunity to meet this responsibility.

The child's first experiences with mathematics instruction in the school is often one of considering sets, subsets, equivalent sets, one-to-one correspondence, and counting. From here the program often moves rapidly to the task of associating numerals with sets, writing numerals, and, before long, to practicing the computational algorithms. From this point on, the danger is in forgetting the relation between the symbolic language being learned and aspects of the real world it is capable of describing.

Attempts to improve this situation are being made in three ways. First, and most frequently found in classrooms today, individual teachers have either made or purchased materials which they have found useful for particular parts of the instructional program. Flannelboards with sets of objects, counting frames and abacus-type materials, place value charts, fraction materials, and geometric shapes are representative of materials found in almost every school and in many classrooms. Used creatively and meaningfully, these materials provide much assistance in the development of mathematics concepts.

Ideally, concepts should be developed first through manipulation of concrete materials and discussion. Symbolic representation of these concepts then follows. As an example, consider introduction to concepts of division with remainders. Using counters of almost any kind (beads, sticks, bottle caps), various situations can be explored. For example, 15 divided by 4 might result in an arrangement as shown in Figure 5-5. Nine divided by 2 is illustrated in b.

```
x x x x
x x x x          x x x x x
x x x x          x x x x
x x x
```

a   *b*

Figure 5-5

In the first example, the idea of division is shown to represent the process of finding how many sets of four are contained in 15. The child will discover that the remaining set has less than 4 objects. This concrete representation can be used before the child begins to represent the idea with numerals. His first representation with numerals may appear as 3 (groups) and 3 (left over).

Dynamic symbolization techniques would permit expressing the result as *he* has developed it. Only after sharing his results with others would the need for a standardized notation become evident. The class could reach some common agreement which in time could be guided by the teacher to desired adult forms.

Here again is a case when the teacher or pupil may wish to turn to the book to find out about the way in which the text treats the matter of reporting results in division. Might it not be as easy to consider problems with remainders even before or at the same time problems without remainders are being considered?

Perhaps because many teachers have found useful ways of providing experiences with multi-sensory materials, some mathematics curriculum programs are built quite extensively around a particular set of multi-sensory materials. The Cuisenaire rods,[11] the structural materials developed by Stern,[12] and the more recent developments by Dienes[13] are representative of such programs. Likely, most teachers will not exclusively use any one of the sets of materials but rather will find effective ways of using them as adjuncts to their own instructional programs.

---

[11]C. Gattegno, "New Developments in Arithmetic Teaching in Britain," *The Arithmetic Teacher*, III (April, 1956), 85-89.

[12]C. Stern, *Children Discover Arithmetic* (New York: Harper & Brothers, 1949).

[13]Z. Dienes and E. W. Golding, *Sets, Numbers, and Powers* (New York: Herder and Herder, 1966).

Finally, the report of multi-sensory materials would not be complete without some mention of the work going on currently in some of the major mathematics curriculum development projects. Mathematicians who turned their attention to the schools in the middle and late 1950's were first concerned primarily with the improvement of the mathematics content. This reform, while not completed by any means, has resulted in considerable change in the content included in mathematics programs in schools at all levels. More recently the attention of these mathematicians has been directed to instructional method. Exploration with ways of relating mathematics to other curriculum areas as in science and social studies is a current emphasis. Relating mathematics to the child's world is receiving increasing amounts of attention. Much work is being done to provide physical materials with which the child may explore mathematical ideas. Davis has developed what he calls his shoe boxes, largely devoted to the inductive discovery of mathematical relationships through their graphs, in each of which is a set of materials and instructions which the child explores with relative independence. Minnemast has experimented with Minibars and various materials useful in the study of symmetry. Educational Services Incorporated has developed a wide range of instructional materials.

Interestingly, these developments make mathematicians appear as "neo-progressives" for it was the Progressives of 30 years ago who sought to relate the school curriculum to the child's world, to relate the various disciplines, and to utilize a wide variety of instructional materials. While they made many useful contributions to the improvement of schools, their primary failure was due to their lack of adequate understanding and appreciation for mathematical content. Interesting to observe for the next few years will be the way in which the neo-progressive mathematicians are able to combine their store of competence with an understanding of child development to improve the nature of learning experiences in the classroom.

All of these materials—textbook, worktext, workbook, and supplementary—provide the teacher with important means to reach important objectives. The list of materials is vast and no attempt has been made here to be exhaustive. Nevertheless, the materials mentioned indicate the scope of what is available and are sufficient to serve many of the needs in today's classrooms. As time permits, the teacher will do well to stay abreast of new developments in this important area of instructional materials. Up-to-date information on this subject is available from the National Council of Teachers of Mathematics and the Report of the International Clearinghouse on Science and Mathematics Curricular Developments, published yearly and available on request.

Topics for Further Investigation

1. How many distinct teaching strategies or methods can you categorize? Characterize the features by which each method can be identified. Can you suggest any general guidelines to fit a method to a kind of mathematical instructional objective? Prepare a lesson plan on a mathematical topic for use in any grade of your own choosing. Indicate how you would use the textbook in connection with the lesson. Try to develop a plan which does not rely on the textbook in the initial teaching phases. What methods, materials, and evaluative techniques will you use? What provisions could you make to individualize instruction?

2. Prepare a brief position paper which frames your attitude toward the role and value of innovation in the classroom. You may wish to cite research or other evidence to support your position. Under what conditions should innovation be undertaken? What moral responsibility is undertaken by the innovator? Is this similar to the professional responsibility assumed by the medical doctor? What should the product of innovation be? How should innovative results be reported? When should an innovative program be terminated, that is, under what conditions?

3. What value do you see in elementary school teachers, teaching several subjects, nevertheless having an area of special competence such as reading or mathematics or social studies, science, or art? What advantages or disadvantages would accrue to the individual teacher and the school if all elementary school teachers had some teaching area specialty?

4. What role should inservice education play in the mathematics program? Do you think that teachers can learn more about content and methods while school is in session? Who should determine the topics and learning activities that should be emphasized in a given inservice program? What is the teacher's role in setting up the mathematics inservice program?

Bibliography

Association for Childhood Education. "Recommended Equipment and Supplies for Nursery, Kindergarten, Primary, and Intermediate Schools." Washington, D.C.: The Association, 1949.

Bloom, B. S. *Taxonomy of Educational Objectives—Handbook I: Cognitive Domain.* New York: Longmans, Green and Co., 1956.

Bruner, J. S. "Needed: A Theory of Instruction," *Educational Leadership,* 20(8), May, 1963, 523-532.

Buffie, E. G., R. C. Welch, and D. D. Paige. *Mathematics: Strategies of Teaching.* Englewood Cliffs, N.J.: Prentice-Hall, Inc., 1968.

Bushnell, D. D. "For Each Student a Teacher," *Saturday Review,* 49(30):31, July 23, 1966.

Davis, R. B. "Discovery in the Teaching of Mathematics," Chapter 8 in *Learning by Discovery: A Critical Appraisal.* L. S. Shulman and E. R. Keislar (eds.). Chicago: Rand McNally & Co., 1966.

DeVault, M. V. *Improving Mathematics Programs.* Columbus, Ohio: Charles E. Merrill, Books, 1961.

Flanders, Ned A. "Teacher-Pupil Contacts and Mental Hygiene," *Journal of Social Issues,* 15(1), 30-39.

Graham, W. A. "Individual Teaching of Fifth- and Sixth-Grade Arithmetic," *The Arithmetic Teacher,* 11(4), April, 1964, 223-234.

Hertz, Pauline. "Manipulative Devices in Lower Grades," *The Arithmetic Teacher,* IV, November, 1957, 214-16.

Holt, John. *How Children Fail.* New York: Pitman, 1964.

Johnson, C. E. "Grouping Children for Arithmetic Instruction," *The Arithmetic Teacher,* I, February, 1954, 16-20.

Krathwohl, D. R. *et al. Taxonomy of Educational Objectives—Handbook II: Affective Domain.* New York: David McKay Company, Inc., 1964.

Lockard, J. D. *Report of the International Clearinghouse on Science and Mathematics Curricular Developments.* Published annually. Available from Science Teaching Center, University of Maryland, College Park, Maryland 20740.

National Council of Teachers of Mathematics. *Instruction in Arithmetic.* The Council. Twenty-Fifth Yearbook. 1960.

National Society for the Study of Education. C. Junge and Metzner, "Instructional Materials for Teaching Arithmetic," *The Teaching of Arithmetic.* Fiftieth Yearbook, 1951, Part II, 155-85.

_____. *Individualizing Instruction.* 1964 Yearbook. Washington, D.C.: The Association, 1964. Association for Supervision and Curriculum Development.

Osborn, Roger, M. V. DeVault, C. C. Boyd, and W. R. Houston, *Extending Mathematics Understanding.* Columbus, Ohio: Charles E. Merrill Books, 1961.

Page, D. *Maneuvers on Lattices.* University of Illinois Arithmetic Project.

_____. *Number Lines, Functions, and Fundamental Topics.* Macmillan, 1964.

Page, David, and UICSM Staff. "Arithmetic with Frames." University of Illinois Arithmetic Project, 1207 West Stoughton Street, Urbana, Illinois.

Reddell, W. D., and M. V. DeVault. "In-Service Research in Arithmetic Teaching Aids," *The Arithmetic Teacher,* VII, May, 1960, 243-47.

Smith, Lewis B. "Pegboard Geometry," *The Arithmetic Teacher,* 12(4), April, 1965, 271-274.

Smith, R. R. "Provisions for Individual Differences," *The Learning of Mathematics, Its Theory and Practice.* National Council of Teachers of Mathematics, Twenty-first Yearbook. Washington, D.C.: The Council, 1953, 271-302.

Stern, C. "The Concrete Devices of Structural Arithmetic," *The Arithmetic Teacher,* V, April, 1948, 119-30.

Tuttle, Ruth H. "Counters? Yes, But . . .," *The Arithmetic Teacher,* V, February, 1958, 25-8.

Weaver, J. F. "Differentiated Instruction in Arithmetic: An Overview and a Promising Trend," *Education,* LXXIV, January, 1954, 300-5.

_____. "Differentiated Instruction and School-Class Organization for Mathematical Learning within the Elementary Grades," *The Arithmetic Teacher,* XIII, October, 1966, 495-506.

_____. "Materials for Manipulation," *Journal of Education,* CXXXVI, October 1953.

6

IMPROVING EVALUATION PROCEDURES

> *We shall not cease from exploration*
> *And the end of all our exploring*
> *Will be to arrive where we started*
> *And know the place for the first time.*
> T. S. *Eliot*, Little Gidding

PURPOSES OF EVALUATION

In Chapter 5 we were concerned mainly with the methods and materials of instruction. We now turn to a third aspect of instruction, evaluation. Every effective teacher automatically and constantly evaluates as a part of daily instructional activities. Through the give-and-take of verbal interaction in the classroom, the teacher obtains a wealth of information concerning the success of the lesson and the quality of the learning taking place. The questions the children raise, the vocabulary they use and misuse, the skills they exhibit, the reasoning patterns they employ, the interest and vitality with which they approach their learning tasks are all examples of immediate feedback which the perceptive teacher detects, evaluates, and uses to improve all aspects of instruction.

This immediate feedback is shown in Figure 6-1 in the path C-1. This important kind of evaluation is unique to the human element in the system. No mechanical system using even the biggest and fastest of modern computers could hope to cope with the vast amount of subjective information which the teacher readily senses in each lesson. We yield perhaps a little in objectivity or precision of measurement in gathering information this way. But we gain some of the most important and crucial kinds of information by attentive *listening to what the children are saying*, by asking them direct questions, and observing what they are doing.

This feedback is first of all the source of immediate modifications in the instructional plans. The teacher adjusts, within certain limits, the immediate learning experience to meet the needs which arise from classroom interaction in spontaneous fashion, needs which no amount of preplanning is likely to have anticipated. The adjustments required may be too great to make on the spot. In such cases, preplanning may have failed to take some vital factor into account; this failure becomes evident as the lesson progresses. By the time of the next lesson, however, this information is used to redesign the instruction, select perhaps a new strategy, or employ different materials.

In the most severe situations, no amount or particular kind of instruction seems to work for certain pupils. This problem, if it involves fundamental ideas, concepts, or structures, requires more extensive evaluation to determine the cause and experimental innovation to explore ways of breaking through the impasse. This link is shown in Figure 6-1 as the paths III-1 and III-2.

Thus, within the instruction component of the curriculum model, it should be evident that one of the most important tasks a teacher must perform is evaluation.

The success of the instructional program is to a large extent dependent upon the effectiveness of the evaluation procedures used. These procedures influence not only the individual classroom but can affect the direction of the entire school mathematics program.

We want to discuss two basic procedures in this chapter: evaluation by teacher-made instruments and evaluation by the use of standardized instruments. *Teacher-made tests* sample instructional objectives. The analysis of pupil performance on these tests can be used by the teacher to adjust certain instructional procedures he may have been using.

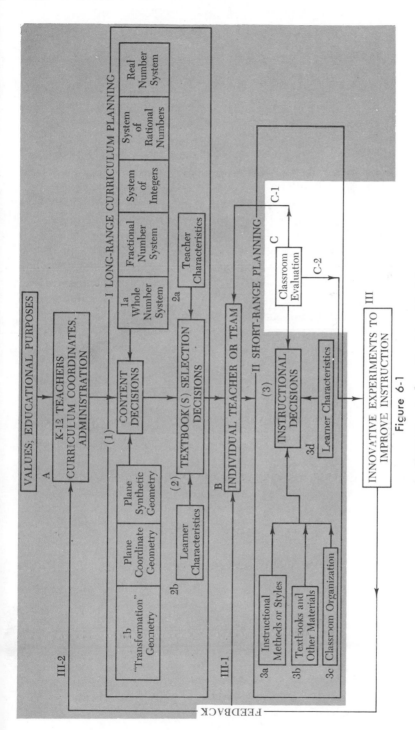

Figure 6-1

An ESM Curriculum Decision Model.

Standardized tests measure performance by age or grade or by ability levels across classrooms. These tests permit assessment of total school performance. Instructional changes may also occur as a result of the analysis of standardized test results. Thus, it is difficult to overemphasize the importance of the teacher's need to know how to test and how to evaluate and analyze the results of testing.

The task of developing effective evaluation procedures is a particularly complex one, in large part because current instructional objectives have gone beyond the earlier goals of speed and accuracy in computation. There is much current concern that we help children learn to think and act like mathematicians, to learn to discover, to use creative approaches to problem solving, and to inquire into the nature of mathematics. These goals have been generally accepted by teachers, but the task of measuring the attainment of these desired behaviors continues to be extremely difficult. The difficulties encountered fall into four categories. Teachers face the problem of relating objectives to tests; of constructing appropriate test items; of selecting appropriate standardized tests; and of analyzing test performance. This chapter has been designed to help the teacher understand the nature of these problems as they pertain to classroom instruction.

Clarification of Objectives through Test Development Activities

One of the values to be derived from efforts to measure mathematical achievement is the clarification of instructional objectives. A carefully designed program of evaluation within a classroom includes a wide variety of measuring instruments and techniques. Such a program includes standardized tests, observations and interview procedures, and teacher-made tests in any of a number of forms. The effectiveness of a teacher's participation in the development of such a program is dependent to a large extent on how carefully he delineates the objectives of his instructional activities.

The relationship between the clarification of objectives and the development of appropriate test items may be illustrated with an example in the area of numeration at the early intermediate grade level. Suppose the children are working in a unit which emphasizes an understanding of numeration systems. The teacher wants to measure not only the children's manipulative ability to change base ten numerals to another base but also their ability to generalize their knowledge about base. How to measure the ability to make generalizations is the test construction problem with which he is confronted.

The numeration system shown in Figure 6-2 provides the basis for the test items he ultimately devised. The children were to identify the base ten numeral which belonged in the appropriate boxes, completing each item in the sequence.

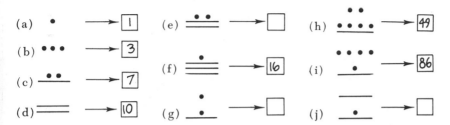

Figure 6-2

The symbols in Figure 6-2 are part of the Mayan numeration system. In this test, the child is given a part of the meaning for the symbols and is then asked to extend what is given by using what he knows about numeration systems in general. If he has an understanding of base and place, he will see in this context that place-value positions are vertical rather than horizontal and that the base is twenty rather than ten. The item *g* is particularly difficult because the learner must see this in context, that is, he must transfer meanings which come before and after *g* to sense that, indeed, this system is base twenty. After *g* has been understood, item *j* tests a further application of this knowledge. This particular item is likely also to teach as it tests, for it further strengthens the child's understanding of base and place ideas. A good test item will usually have this "teaching" characteristic built into it, as we see next.

Teaching through Testing

Effective evaluation procedures can teach new concepts. The point that an effective test should teach is made by Stroud:

> It is probably not extravagant to say that the contribution made to a student's store of knowledge by the taking of an examination is as great, minute for minute, as any other enterprise he engages in.[1]

---

[1]James B. Stroud, *Psychology in Education* (New York: David McKay Co., 1946), p. 476.

The "teaching potential" of a test can be enhanced in several ways. In addition to the value derived by the student from his participation in taking the test, the manner in which the teacher reacts to the pupil's test performance will determine the extent of additional values. Classroom or individual discussion of the results of a test increase learning also.

One example of the relationship between teaching and testing is found in programed instruction. The continuous interplay between informational statements, questions, and pupil responses in a programed sequence is shown in Figure 6-3.[2]

Set A   Set B

1. Look at the pictures of sets shows above. Set A is a set of *animals* whose *members* are named cat, pig, dog, and _____.
2. Set A is a set of animals whose _____ are named cat, pig, dog, and horse.
3. Set A is a set whose members are all _____.
4. Set B is a set of *animals* whose *members* are named _____ and _____.
5. The _____ of Set B are named dog and horse.
6. Dog and horse are the names of *all* the members of Set _____.
7. Dog is the name of a member of Set A, and dog is *also* the name of a member of Set _____.
8. Horse is the name of a member of Set B, and horse is *also* the name of a member of Set _____.

Figure 6-3

In this programed sequence, the question represented by each open sentence has been answered in the statements immediately before it. The same kind of sequence can be used in classroom discourse, giving the teacher an opportunity to evaluate the nature of the child's learning as he teaches. In this way, both evaluation in the formal context of

[2]From *Mathematics Enrichment, Program B* by George Spooner, © 1962 by Harcourt, Brace & World, Inc. and reprinted with their permission.

tests designed to measure achievement and informal dialog become essential parts of the total instruction program.

Measuring Achievement

Likely the most frequently used teacher-made test is one in which the ideas and concepts in the unit just completed are evaluated. Included in such tests are items which evaluate (1) the pupils' ability to recall certain aspects of the unit, (2) his understanding of concepts included in the unit, and (3) his ability to transfer these understandings to new situations. The examples in Figure 6-4 illustrate learning at these three levels following instruction in multiplying by multiples of ten.

1. (a) $10 \times 36 =$ _____   Rote use of the idea of multiplying by powers of ten.

    (b) $100 \times 132 =$ _____

    (c) $1000 \times 1{,}567 =$ _____

2.

$$24\overline{)5088}$$ with quotient 2 and 48 below

(a) What does this numeral represent?
   (1) 2×24
   (2) 20×24
   (3) 200×24

Understanding the use of multiples of ten.

---

3. (a) $60 \div 10 =$ _____

   (b) $350 \div 50 =$ _____   Extending the idea of multiplying by multiples of ten to division.

   (c) $4100 \div 10 =$ _____

   (d) $3600 \div 200 =$ _____

   (e) $420 \div 100 =$ _____

Evaluating Different Levels of Learning

Figure 6-4

The first example in Figure 6-4 represents a question at the recall or rote memory level. Terminology, definition of terms, or application of a concept or generalization in the same context in which it was taught are examples of content for questions at this level. Question 1 in

Figure 6-4 is a recall question if children have been taught to annex zeros when multiplying by powers of ten. Understanding and application are both represented in the second item as the use of multiples of ten in the division algorithm is called for. Finally, item 3 requires the transfer of previously learned material, including the multiplication by multiples of ten, to a series of items representing a new kind of situation, division by multiples of ten. Transfer has become of increasing concern in evaluation as it has evolved into a central position in the behavioral objectives associated with modern instruction.

THE ROLE OF BEHAVIORAL OBJECTIVES

Although one of the major educational emphases of the 1960's is that of behavioral objectives, the idea that objectives should be defined in terms of desired behavior is not new. Tyler[3] discussed this problem more than 35 years ago and made the point that the purpose of education was not to accumulate knowledge but to change behavior. Yet only recently has this idea had an impact on evaluation instruments and procedures. Much of the current impetus has both resulted in and grown out of the publication by Bloom and others of the *Taxonomy of Educational Objectives*.[4]

The use of behavioral objectives as the central point in evaluation has an advantage which results from thoughtful consideration of the interrelatedness of objectives, instruction, and evaluation. As indicated in the following list of behavioral objectives and sample test suggestions[5] for measuring each objective (Figure 6-5), both what is to be taught and the behavior which should result from the instruction is included in the statement of the objective. The illustrations include topics in numeration, fractions, systems of measurement, subtraction, multiplication, and geometry.

Notwithstanding the widespread support given the use of behavioral objectives, their exclusive use in building evaluative instruments is questioned by some. Certainly their use has resulted in improved clarity in statements of objectives, but one must be careful that the objectives of instruction do not result in an educational focus which is

---

[3]Ralph W. Tyler, "A Generalized Technique for Constructing Achievement Tests," *Educational Research Bulletin*, The Ohio State University, Columbus, Ohio, X, 1931.

[4]Benjamin S. Bloom, *et al. Taxonomy of Educational Objectives* (New York: David McKay Co., 1956).

[5]These behavioral objectives and sample test items are drawn from some of the early work of the University of Pittsburgh, Research and Development Center on Individualization of Instruction.

Figure 6-5

Behavioral Objective	*Sample Test Item*

Numeration

Responds to questions related to the number sequence, 1 to 10, for example, tells what number comes before, after a given number, or in between two numbers.

"What number comes just before 8, just after 9, in between 7 and 9?"

Selects which of two (or three) numbers is greater (greatest), smaller (smallest) for numbers to 100. Places >, < between two numerals to indicate the greater or less.

"Place > or < in the boxes."

45 ☐ 37   86 ☐ 98

23 ☐ 18

Completes exercises for skip-counting by 2's, 5's, and 10's; limit of 200.

"Find the missing numbers." 8, 10, 12, ___, 16, 18, 20, ___; 15, 17, ___, 21, 23, 25, ___, 29.

Completes patterns for skip counting by 3's and 4's from any starting point.

"Complete the pattern:" 360, 363, ___, ___, ___, 375, ___.

Uses the information that there are 3 feet in 1 yard and 36 inches in 1 yard to solve problems which require converting yards into feet or inches.

"Jack's toy car went 39 inches. Bill's toy car went 1 yard. Jack's car went how many inches further than Bill's car?"

Writes the correct decimal fractions for a common or mixed fraction having a denominator of either ten or one hundred and vice versa.

"Write the equivalent decimal fraction."

$7/10 = $ _____

$47\ 5/10 = $ _____

$864\ 9/100 = $ _____

"Write the equivalent fraction."

$.86 = 86/100$

$1.9 = $ _____

$32.85 = $ _____

Locates the prime numbers to 100 on a chart by the definition that: "a prime number is one which has exactly two, different, whole-number factors."

"Circle the prime numbers on the chart."

Adds and subtracts one and two digit numbers in base five without using expanded notation.

"Do the following without expanding:"

32_{five} 23_{five}

$+11_{five}$ -14_{five}
_____   _____

Fractions

Divides an object or set of objects in "half" and identifies "one-half" of an object or set of objects.

"Divide this pie in half. Divide this set of cookies in half."

Finds the least common multiple for a given set of whole numbers and finds the LCM for a given set of fractions.

"Find the least common multiple of the set:"

[12, 10, 18]

Systems of Measurement

Utilizes the information that there are 12 inches in a foot (footruler) to make comparisons, such as "which is greater: 7 inches or 1 foot?"

"Circle the greater length."

9 inches   1 foot

Multiplication

Uses the distributive principle with single digit factors to simplify multiplication problems; for example, 9 x 3 = (8 + 1) x 2.

"Complete each equation:"
$$5 \times 2 = (4 + 1) \times 2$$
$$= (4 \times 2) + (1 \times 2)$$
$$= \underline{\hspace{1cm}} + \underline{\hspace{1cm}}$$
$$= \underline{\hspace{1cm}}$$

Uses the distributive principle to simplify multiplication of one and two digit numbers; for example, 7 x 85 = (7 x 80) + (7 x 5).

"Fill in each frame."
$$5 \times 3 = (4 \times 3) + (1 \times 3) =$$
$$\square + \square = \square$$
$$12 \times 2 = (10 \times 2) + \square \times 2 =$$
$$\square + \square = \square$$

Geometry

Identifies open and closed curves; straight lines and line segments; and "square corners." Also, names points in a line and names line segments.

"Mark an X on the curve which is an open curve."

Identifies a right angle and names angles by three points, for example, angle ABC.

"Select the picture which shows a right angle. Write the name of the angle."

Uses a 1-cubic-inch square as a model to find volumes of simple solids. Solves simple volume problems.

Finds circumference and area of a circle using the formulas, $C = 3 = 2r$, and $A = r^2$.

"How many 1-inch cubes will fit in the following solid?"

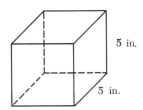

5 in.

5 in.

"What is the circumference of a circle with a radius of 4 inches?"

"What is the area?"

Subtraction

Subtracts two negative numbers using a number line and/or thermometer if necessary.

"Do the following with the aid of the number line:"

$(-5) - (-2) = $ _____ (-10)
                                                $-(-8)$

too narrow. Ebel sounds a word of warning to indicate that in a rapidly changing, highly complex world, the kind of behavior which might be required only a few years hence is difficult to predict. He suggests that a better definition of educational objectives is in terms of "relevant and powerful knowledge, the command of which seems well calculated to give the scholar the capacity to adapt his behavior effectively in the face of a complexity of varied, changing situations."[6] The implication of Ebel's statement is that evaluation techniques must include but go beyond paper-and-pencil tests designed around behavioral objectives. Thus, we turn now to a consideration of various techniques which are important to the classroom teacher as he designs a comprehensive evaluation program.

TECHNIQUES IN EVALUATION

Techniques available to classroom teachers include evaluation as a part of teaching, observation and interviews, teacher-made tests, and standardized tests. Any comprehensive, effective program of measurement and evaluation will utilize all four of these procedures in an

---

[6]Robert L. Ebel, *Measuring Educational Achievement* (Englewood Cliffs, N.J.: Prentice-Hall, Inc., 1965), p. 36.

attempt to obtain a full picture of the achievement and on-going progress of an individual learner.

Evaluation as a Part of Teaching

Undoubtedly the most famous of all testers was Socrates. His teaching method relied solely on a kind of dialogue between teacher and student in which the teacher asked questions and the pupil answered. So sensitive was Socrates to the individual pupil and to his responses that he was able to pose a series of questions which led his charge to new insights and understandings. With the same goal in mind, classroom teachers today use a questioning approach in teaching (1) to determine what knowledge the learner now has, and (2) to evoke a thoughtful approach toward the new knowledge to be understood.

As Bloom[7] and Saunders[8] have pointed out, the nature of classroom questions should reflect the objectives of instruction. The following questions illustrate the kind which might possibly be asked by the teacher during a sequence of lessons on sets.

1. What is a set? (Give examples of well-defined and ambiguously defined sets and ask, "Is this a set"?)

2. What are two techniques we sometimes use to represent a set?

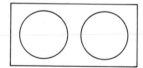 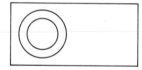 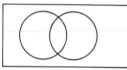

3. Which Venn Diagram represents the set of all even numbers and the set of all odd numbers?

4. Which Venn Diagram could be used to represent the Set of Prime Numbers between 1 and 20 and the Set of Even numbers between 1 and 20? What numbers are in the intersection of the two sets?

5. What kind of triangle can be formed by the union of three line segments of equal length?

6. Describe the set consisting of the intersection of any two of the line segments forming that triangle.

---

[7]Bloom, *op. cit.*

[8]Norris Saunders, *Classroom Questions: What Kinds?* (New York: Harper & Row, 1966).

7. Describe the intersection of a plane and a line which is not parallel to that plane.

8. Describe the intersection of two non-parallel planes.

9. What are the possible geometric figures formed by the intersection of a cube and a plane which is not parallel to any one side of the cube?

The first question in the series requires simple recall of a definition. The second is of the same type, emphasizing symbolization agreements. From there on, however, the sequence of questions requires the use and application of previously acquired knowledge with the new understanding of sets. For children who have not previously studied this topic, questions 7, 8, and 9 require a thoughtful analysis of the situation, drawing upon what has been previously learned and applying these understandings to new situations. Not only does the final question evoke a thoughtful response, but it might also require the use of sketches or pupil-constructed three-dimensional models before pupils are satisfied with their own answers and the answers of their classmates.

There seems to be little question but that the quality of instruction improves as the proportion of questions changes from rote to those which require analysis, interpretation, and translations of previously learned information to new situations. As the focus of instruction changes, so must the questions, both at the time of instruction and at the time of testing.

Observations and Interview Procedures

With the increasing use of individualized instruction in elementary school classrooms, the teacher is often in a one-to-one relationship with the learner. The opportunities for observation of the individual child during large-group instruction, however, should not be overlooked. The sensitive teacher observes, and mentally records, the kinds of responses made by individual pupils. He recognizes that during a discussion one particular child responds at a sophisticated level, whereas another demonstrated consistently immature patterns of response. Likewise, during the work period, the teacher takes every possible opportunity to observe the individual child at work. The teacher seeks to determine to what extent the pupil must rely on concrete materials. Does the child use pencil illustrations to find problem solutions? Does the child draw pictures of mathematical situations which really do represent the mathematical problem faced? What crutches does the child rely on? How independently does the child work? These questions are important because their answers provide the direction which guides the teacher who would help each learner move to improved understanding and appreciation of mathematics.

Concern has been increasing for improved understanding of the way children think about mathematics. Various interview and recording procedures are particularly helpful in the collection and organization of this kind of information. Weaver[9] has reported a useful procedure a teacher used to determine the thought patterns of her fourth graders at the beginning of the year prior to her instructional program in multiplication. Her interviews were centered around pupil responses to known and unknown multiplication facts which were presented on 3 x 5 cards. A record of responses was kept and summarized in the manner shown in Figure 6-6.

A review of the information in Figure 6-6 indicates that all children were able to answer the first question, 7×3, correctly; all but one answered the second, 8×4, correctly; and all but one also correctly responded to the "untaught" fact. On any paper-and-pencil test all of these children except Jerry would look much alike; they correctly answered all questions. Yet on closer examination, it can be seen that their approaches differed considerably from one another. Herein lies the "big dividends from little interviews," as Weaver calls them, for when the teacher recognizes the thought processes used by children, he is in a position to understand and to direct their further development.

Another interesting approach to the task of recording information gained from interviews was developed by Gray.[10] He was concerned with the topic of multiplication and with the process which learners used as they attempted to solve examples which they had not been taught. The schematic presentation shown in Figure 6-7 made it possible for him to record in a somewhat objective fashion the variety of responses made by the learner. In this instance, he was attempting to obtain responses which would indicate the child's understanding and ability to use appropriately the distributive property of multiplication. Previously taught facts included 6×2, 7×3, and 9×4. Untaught combinations included 24×4, and 7×6.

Both the Weaver and the Gray systems are reported here as examples of the kinds of systems which have been used successfully and, there-

[9]J. F. Weaver, "Big Dividends from Little Interviews," *The Arithmetic Teacher*, II (April, 1955), 40-47.

[10]Roland F. Gray, "An Approach to Evaluating Arithmetic Understandings," *The Arithmetic Teacher*, XIII (March, 1966), 187-191.

Pupil	Previously "Taught" Facts		"Untaught" Fact
	$\begin{array}{r} 7 \\ \times 3 \\ \hline \end{array}$	$8 \times 4 =$	$\begin{array}{r} 9 \\ \times 5 \\ \hline \end{array}$
Sally	Automatic Response Correct Product	Hesitated, then recited full "table": 1 × 4 = 4, 2 × 4 = 8, 3 × 4 = 12, etc. to 8 × 4 = 32.	Hesitated, saying "I don't know that." Then put down 5 rows of 9 dots and counted by ones to reach 45.
David	Automatic Response Correct Product	Said, "Let's see: 6 fours are 24, 7 fours are 28, 8 fours are 32. That's it."	Looked up a bit, then said, "Now I know how to work that one! 5 tens are 50, so take away 5 and that's 45."
Linda	Hesitated, then said: "7 and 7 are 14—15, 16—17, 18 —19, 20—21."	Hesitated, then said: "Oh, I know! It's the same as 4 eights, and I remember that's 32."	Hesitated, saying "We never had that one before." Began to add 9 and 9; then suddenly she stopped and counted by fives to 45.
Carole	Automatic Response Correct Product	With seemingly no hesitation, said: "4 fours are 16; and 10, that's 26; and 6 more —30, 32."	Very little hesitation, then said: "Well, 4 nines are 36; and 10, that's 46; so take away 1, that's 45."
Jerry	Automatic Response	Automatic response, but incorrect product of 36. When asked to "prove" it, looked puzzled and said, "I can't, but I'm sure that's what it is—36."	Looked very confused saying: "I don't remember *that* one. Did we have it before?" Was unable to attack it sensibly, asking: "Is it near 14?"

Figure 6-6

Illustrative Summary of Thought Patterns.

fore may serve as models after which teachers might pattern their own interview recording systems. In any case, interview procedures require careful planning and organization if the data gathered are to provide for effective direction of future instructional activity.

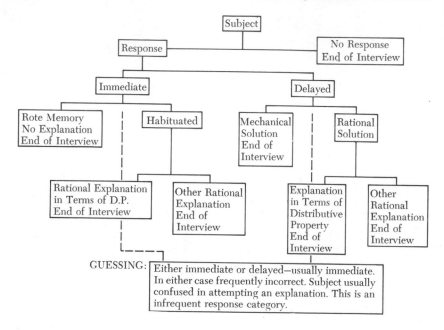

Figure 6-7

A schematic representation of scoring procedures for the individual interview inventory of arithmetic understandings.

Teacher-made Tests

The most frequently used evaluation procedure is that of the teacher-made test. An important characteristic of the teacher-made test is relevance. The test must be relevant to the objectives of instruction. The objectives of instruction, it will be remembered, include both content objectives and behavioral objectives. The test must reflect more than the content which has been taught. It must also reflect the behavior which has been sought through the efforts of instruction. This behavior, as has been pointed out, ranges from simple recall or rote memory to higher levels of thought including analysis, application, and evaluation.[11]

A number of test items are included in Figure 6-8 to illustrate each level of the cognitive taxonomy. It should be recognized that the cognitive level of an item is a relative matter. This relativity is readily

---

[11]Bloom, *op. cit.*

illustrated in computational items. In the test item, "Find the sum of 24 and 29," the level of thought required obviously depends on the past learning experience of the child. For the fifth grader, this item will be a mechanical or memory item if he has mastered both the addition facts and the addition algorithm involving the regrouping idea. For the second grader, however, this same question poses a kind of problem he has not yet encountered and his performance gives a clue to his problem-solving ability, his tendency to explore novel mathematical situations, his use of paper-and-pencil sketches or concrete objects to illustrate the problem, and his understanding of ways of renaming numbers. All of these understandings cannot be observed by use of a simple multiple-choice, true-false, or short-answer question. In such cases, comprehensive evaluation of his learning requires that his exploratory efforts on paper or with materials be recorded. A wide variety of test item types which have been found useful to teachers in the construction of classroom tests have been included in Figure 6-8.

Figure 6-8

Illustrative Teacher-Made Test Items

Sets
A. Complete the following:
   (1) The set of even numbers from 1-15 =
       {——, ——, ——, ——, ——, ——, ——}
   (2) The set of odd numbers from 10-20 =
       {——, ——, ——, ——, ——}
   (3) The set of numbers between 1 and 20 which are multiples of three =
       {——, ——, ——, ——, ——, ——}
B. Which set is the intersection of Sets A and B?
       A = {3, 6, 9, 12, 15}   B = {2, 4, 6, 8, 10}
   (1) A ∩ B = {3, 6, 10}
   (2) A ∩ B = {2, 3, 6, 8, 9, 10, 12, 15}
   (3) A ∩ B = {2, 4, 6, 8, 10}
   (4) A ∩ B = {6}
C. Mark each statement true or false as indicated in the Venn Diagram.

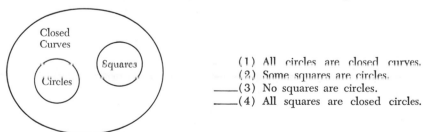

(1) All circles are closed curves.
(2) Some squares are circles.
___(3) No squares are circles.
___(4) All squares are closed circles.

Figure 6-8 (Continued)

D. Draw Venn Diagrams for each of the following sets.
  A = All animals
  B = All mammals
  C = All domesticated animals

Numeration

A. Complete the following.
  (1) 326 = _____ hundreds _____ tens _____ ones
  (2) 418 = _____ hundreds   11   tens _____ ones
  (3) 532 = _____ hundreds _____ tens   12   ones
  (4) 757 =   6   hundreds _____ tens   7   ones

B. Match with each Roman Numeral the equivalent Hindu-Arabic Numeral.
  _____(1) XXXIII   a. 24
  _____(2) IL   b. 33
  _____(3) XXIV   c. 55
  _____(4) LV   d. 49

C. Complete the sequence of Roman Numerals.
  II, IV, ____, VIII, X, ____, ____, XVI, ____, ____

D. In solving the subtraction problem, 243 − 28 = □ which of the following
  names for 243 is most useful?
  (1) 2 hundred   4 tens   3 ones
  (2) 1 hundred 14 tens   3 ones
  (3) 2 hundred   3 tens 13 ones
  (4) 1 hundred 13 tens   3 ones

E. Write a paragraph discussing whether or not it matters if one multiplies first
  or adds first in the sentence $4 + 6 \times 7 = \square$

Prime Numbers

A. Each of the following is a prime number. True or False.
  _____(1)   14
  _____(2)   37
  _____(3)   51
  _____(4)   83

B. Circle the common multiples of each pair of numbers. Underline the least
  common multiple in each set.
  2, 3 → {4, 6, 8, 10, 12, 14, 16, 18, 20, 22, 24}
  3, 4 → {6, 8, 9, 12, 15, 16, 18, 20, 21, 24, 27}
  4, 5 → {8, 10, 12, 15, 16, 20, 24, 25, 28, 30, 32}

C. Which of the following is the product of three primes?
  (1)   6
  (2) 16
  (3) 24
  (4) 35

D. What is a prime number?

Geometry

A. Name each of the following.
  (1) •——————•→   _____
  (2) •——————•   _____
  (3) ←—•——————•→   _____

Figure 6-8 (Continued)

(4) 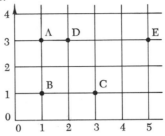 _____

B. Match each point with a number name.
 (1) (3, 1) _____
 (2) (5, 3) _____
 (3) (1, 1) _____
 (4) (1, 3) _____
 (5) (2, 3) _____

C. Which names the volume of the figure?
 (1) 480
 (2) 464
 (3) 448
 (4) 432

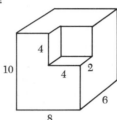

D. Discuss the difference between isosceles, equilateral, and right triangles.

Creative Numeration

Consider a numeration system which utilizes only the following symbols.

$$\cdot = 0$$
$$\backslash = 1$$
$$\vee = 2$$
$$\wedge = 3$$
$$W = 4$$

A. Complete the following sequence.

$$\backslash, \vee, -, W, \backslash\cdot, \backslash\backslash, -, -, \backslash W, -, -, \vee\vee$$

B. True or False.
 ____(1) $\vee + \vee = W$
 ____(2) $W + \wedge = \backslash\backslash$
 ____(3) $\vee\wedge + \backslash W - W\wedge$
 ____(4) $\backslash\wedge + \vee\wedge\backslash - W\vee$

C. Complete each statement.
 (1) $\backslash\wedge + \vee W = $ _____
 (2) $W\vee - \backslash\vee = $ _____

Figure 6-8 (Continued)

(3) \/\ \/\ × \/\ = _____
(4) \ · \/\ ÷ \/\/ = _____

D. Which shows the answer reduced to lowest terms?

(1) $\frac{W}{\mathcal{W}}$
(2) $\frac{\lambda}{V}$
(3) $\frac{W}{VW}$
(4) $\frac{}{VV}$

$$\frac{\mathcal{W}}{\mathcal{W}} + \frac{\lambda}{\mathcal{W}} = \_\_\_\_$$

E. Discuss some of the advantages and disadvantages of this numeration system.

Short-answer completion-type items are probably the most frequently used. They have the advantage of requiring the child to express himself directly rather than through some choice in which he might be guessing among equally unfamiliar alternatives. A creative response is more likely to be observed in a completion-type question than in some other types.

Multiple-choice and true-false items are more objectively scored than certain open-ended kinds of questions. In both types of questions a predictable proportion of correct answers occurs by chance. For instance, if there are 5 choices per item and 20 items on the test, a score of 4 or less would indicate only random selection of answers by the pupil. Good tests should result in mean scores that are well above the random guessing level.

Much more difficult to score and, for that reason, seldom used in mathematics are essay-type questions. Nonetheless, they provide a rich source of information about the learner in terms of the way he constructs his own response. Several examples of essay questions are provided in Figure 6-8.

The type of test item used at any given time will depend on many things. First, it will depend to some extent on the major purpose the evaluation is designed to serve. If the evaluation is being made at the end of a major unit of study and is undertaken primarily for the purpose of determining how much learning has taken place and will be the basis for some form of ranking of pupils and grade assignment, the more objective types, multiple choice and true-false, may be most useful. If, on the other hand, the purpose of evaluation at this particular time is to improve the teacher's perception of the children's understandings and learning processes in regard to previously taught materials, the subjective forms of the completion or essay-type questions may prove to be most useful.

The illustrative items shown in Figure 6-8 are provided for the purpose of showing a wide variety of item types.

Standardized Tests

Standardized tests are widely used for a number of reasons. Usually, (1) they have been carefully prepared, (2) their validity and reliability has been carefully determined, (3) alternate forms of the test are available, and (4) norms have been made available. Each of these characteristics of standardized tests will be considered through a discussion of a test developed under the direction of one of the authors: the Wisconsin Contemporary Test of Elementary Mathematics (WCTEM).[12] Since this test was prepared in answer to the need for a measure of the mathematics taught in contemporary mathematics programs, it is representative of the several new tests currently available to measure the new objectives of elementary school mathematics programs.

Care in Preparation

In addition to the authors of the test who are mathematics educators and curriculum specialists, a number of experts in the measurement field and in mathematics served as consultants in the development of the test. Statistical consultants were concerned with matters pertaining to the difficulty of the items, the relationship of each item to the total test score, and the relative strength of each of the alternative answers in the multiple-choice questions.

A large number of test items were originally prepared and were reviewed by specialists in testing and by mathematicians. Pilot tests were then prepared and tried with samples of third-, fourth-, fifth-, and sixth-grade children. From the analyses of these pilot tests, decisions were made relative to the retention or rejection of each individual item.

Validity and Reliability

Validity refers to the extent to which the instrument measures what it is designed to measure. Several kinds of validity are oftentimes discussed and used in test development. In the case of the WCTEM, *content validity* received especially careful attention. Because the test is reportedly designed to measure the content which is common to the

---

[12]M. Vere DeVault, E. Fennema, K. A. Neufeld, and L. B. Smith, *Wisconsin Contemporary Test of Elementary Mathematics: Manual* (Princeton, N.J.: Personnel Press, 1968).

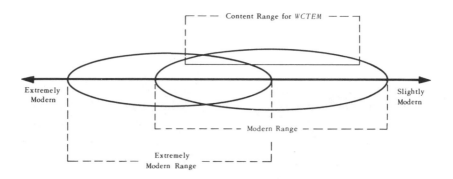

Pictorial Representation Showing
Segment of Modernity Range from Which
WISCONSIN CONTEMPORARY TEST OF ELEMENTARY MATHEMATICS
Items were Drawn

Figure 6-9

Pictorial Representation Showing
Segment of Modernity Range from Which
WISCONSIN CONTEMPORARY TEST OF ELEMENTARY
MATHEMATICS
Items were Drawn

several new programs (WCTEM Manual), items were selected only if they were representative of the content taught in these new programs.[13]

Reliability refers to the likelihood that the test would result in the same score if the measurement were repeated on the same individual at a given time. Measures of reliability of tests range up to .99 in near-perfect cases. The WCTEM reliability data range from .85 to .89 which is considered to be satisfactory for this type of test.

Alternate Forms

The two forms of the test at each pair of grade levels (Form A, Grades 3-4; Form B, Grades 5-6) make it possible for a given teacher or school to use one form of the test early in the year and another form later to determine the amount of growth which has taken place during the year. This change in scores can be useful only to the extent

---

[13]Op. cit., p. 9.

that we are sure that if no growth is made, the test scores would be similar.

Availability of Norms

Grade-level norms have been established for this test for two times in the school year. While most tests are normed at a given time for use over the next several years, fall norms and spring norms for the WCTEM are made available annually. With the rapidly changing nature of mathematics instruction in the elementary schools, it is anticipated that any norms developed for a contemporary test at any one time will not necessarily be appropriate at a later time, even one or two years hence. Thus, the regular renorming of WCTEM was felt to be a much needed feature. The data in Figure 6-10 include the 1967 Spring Percentile Rank norms based on Facts, Concepts, and Total Score for the WCTEM.[14] From this information one can see, for instance, that a third grader with a total score of 43 would be at the 94th percentile rank, above the third quartile score of 36, and in the seventh stanine range.

Use of Standardized Tests

In many schools, tests are administered in the fall soon after school opens and again in the spring somewhat before school closes. This scheduling provides a variety of useful measures. First, the progress of each child has been assessed and can be evaluated in terms of the expectations for that individual. Oftentimes, results obtained from standardized tests are recorded on the pupil's cumulative record so that his progress over a period of several years can be charted. Second, the mean scores for the class on standardized tests provide the teacher with a measure of the gains made over the period of the year. Oftentimes, this information can be used to help an individual teacher appraise his own efforts with the class. If scores turn out to be low, he may seek help from many sources to strengthen his instruction. Also, this school-wide examination of results may assist in the identification of a type of school within the system which is doing less well than might be expected and so additional examination of the problems of instruction in these schools is undertaken. Finally, a system-wide evaluation makes it possible to examine the mathematics program in the total system as compared to national norms. Most standardized

---

[14]Op. cit., p. 28.

PERCENTILE RANK NORMS, BY GRADE AND FORM
SPRING TESTING

SCORE	FACTS						CONCEPTS						TOTAL					
	GRADE 3		GRADE 4		GR.5	GR.6	GRADE 3		GRADE 4		GR.5	GR.6	GRADE 3		GRADE 4		GR.5	GR.6
	Form A	Form B	Form A	Form B	Form A or B	Form A or B	Form A	Form B	Form A	Form B	Form A or B	Form A or B	Form A	Form B	Form A	Form B	Form A or B	Form A or B
55+																	99	99
54																		98
53																		97
52																		96
51																99	99	94
50																97	98	93
49														99	99	95	98	91
48														98	97	93	97	88
47													99	97	95	89	96	86
46													98	96	93	86	95	83
45													97	95	89	82	94	80
44													96	93	86	78	92	77
43													95	91	82	73	91	74
42													93	88	78	69	89	71
41													91	85	73	64	86	68
40													88	82	69	59	84	65
39													85	77	64	55	82	62
38													82	73	59	51	79	59
37													77	69	55	47	76	55
36													73	65	51	42	73	52
35													69	60	47	37	69	49
34													65	56	42	33	66	46
33													60	51	37	30	63	43
32													56	47	33	26	59	40
31													51	43	30	23	55	36
30													47	39	26	20	52	33
29						99						99	43	34	23	17	48	30
28						98						99	39	30	20	14	45	27
27						96						98	34	27	17	12	41	24
26	99	99	99	97	99	93			99	99	99	96	30	24	14	10	38	22
25	99	97	97	91	98	88			99	98	98	93	27	21	12	8	34	19
24	97	92	91	82	96	83		99	98	94	97	89	24	18	10	7	31	17
23	92	85	82	71	94	78	99	98	94	90	96	85	21	15	8	5	27	15
22	85	77	71	61	91	73	98	96	90	85	93	81	18	13	7	4	24	13
21	77	69	61	50	88	67	96	93	85	79	90	75	15	11	5	3	22	11
20	69	59	50	40	83	61	93	90	79	72	87	68	13	9	4	2	19	9
19	59	50	40	31	78	55	90	86	72	64	82	61	11	7	3	2	16	7
18	50	42	31	23	73	49	86	80	64	57	76	54	9	5	2	1	13	6
17	42	34	23	17	67	43	80	74	57	50	69	48	7	4	2		11	5
16	34	27	17	13	61	37	74	67	50	43	63	41	5	3	1		9	4
15	27	20	13	9	55	32	67	60	43	36	56	36	4	3			7	3
14	20	15	9	7	48	26	60	52	36	29	48	30	3	2			5	2
13	15	12	7	4	42	21	52	44	29	23	41	25	3	1			4	2
12	12	9	4	3	36	16	44	36	23	18	34	20	2				3	1
11	9	6	3	2	30	13	36	29	18	14	27	15	1				2	
10	6	4	2	1	23	10	29	23	14	10	21	11					1	
9	4	3	1		18	7	23	17	10	7	16	8						
8	3	2			14	5	17	13	7	5	11	5						
7	2	1			10	3	13	9	5	3	8	4						
6	1				7	2	9	6	3	2	5	2						
5					4	1	6	4	2	1	3	1						
4					2		4	2	1		2							
3					1		2	1			1							
2							1											

Tinted blocks represent maximum scores.

Figure 6-10

Percentile Rank Norms, by Grade and Form, Spring Testing.

tests are normed tests and thus one is able to determine the extent to which a particular grade-level mean is at, above, or below the norms.

This ranking in itself, it must be said, does not answer the question as to whether or not achievement is adequate. Many complex problems intervene to reduce the significance of such a simple analysis of the problem. It should be recognized that national norms report what *is*, not what *should be* the level of achievement. Additionally, the particular characteristics of the pupil population in a given school or school system influence the expectations of results for that school in comparison with national norms. Finally, the objectives of the mathematics program may vary from system to system and the task of determining the extent to which a given test measures the objectives sought is not a simple one.

Many aids in test acquisition and construction are available to teachers. *The Mental Measurements Yearbook,* edited by Buros, provides current appraisals of standardized tests in many areas including mathematics. For the reader interested in looking at older standards and emphases in testing, see the *Twenty-Ninth Yearbook* of the National Society for the Study of Education, Part I, 1930 for comparative purposes. The *Twenty-Sixth Yearbook* of the National Council of Teachers of Mathematics is a useful recent account of methods of evaluating ESM achievement especially. Some strong words cautioning against the dangers of testing are found in the CCSM report.[15] Also, Davis's report on the Madison Project[16] has some fine observations on the place and value of testing, especially in regard to restraint in the evaluation of student efforts. A booklet soon to be published by NCTM entitled, *Mathematics Tests Available in the United States* (Sheldon S. Myers and Floyd G. Delon, authors), offers a comprehensive, up-to-date source of evaluative materials, including tests designed to accompany specific textbooks.

opics for Further Investigation

1. Select a few recent standardized tests designed to measure learning in contemporary mathematics curricula. Compare and contrast

[15]Cambridge Conference School Mathematics, *Goals for School Mathematics* (Boston: Houghton Mifflin, 1963), pp. 29-30.

[16]R. B. Davis, *A Modern Mathematics Program as It Pertains to the Interrelationship of Mathematical Content, Teaching Methods, and Classroom Atmosphere* (The Madison Project), Cooperative Research Project No. D-093 (Syracuse University and Webster College, 1965), pp. 99-105.

information given in the manual in regard to reliability, validity, norms, and objectives emphasized in the test preparation.

2. Using the Twenty-Sixth Yearbook of the National Council of Teachers of Mathematics as a guide, prepare a brief test segment of multiple-choice items. Try to first prepare behavioral objectives in connection with a selected mathematical idea, then design the test items to measure the desired behaviors. If possible, administer the test to a group of children who have an appropriate background and analyze the effectiveness of the distractors used in each item.

3. Select several popular standardized tests and rate them according to the "Standards for Educational and Psychological Tests and Manuals" published by the American Psychological Association (1200 Seventeenth Street, N.W., Washington, D.C. 20036), 1966.

4. What is meant by "form associated" reliability and "time associated" reliability in regard to the characteristics of a standardized test?

5. How would a teacher-made skill achievement test differ from an inventory diagnostic or readiness test? Can you construct test items which might be characteristic of each type?

Bibliography

Bloom, B. S. *Taxonomy of Educational Objectives—Handbook I: Cognitive Domain.* New York: David McKay Co., 1956.

Brueckner, L. J. "Intercorrelations of Arithmetical Abilities," *Journal of Experimental Education*, III, September, 1934.

Buros, O. K. *The Sixth Mental Measurements Yearbook.* Highland Park, N.J.: Gryphon Press, 1965.

Coddington, Earl A. "Scholastic Aptitude Tests in Mathematics," *The American Mathematical Monthly*, August-September, 1963, 750-755.

Dutton, W. H. *Evaluating Pupils' Understanding of Arithmetic.* Englewood Cliffs, N.J.: Prentice-Hall, 1964.

Ebel, Robert L. *Measuring Educational Achievement.* Englewood Cliffs, N.J.: Prentice-Hall, 1965.

Findley, W. G. "Educational and Psychological Testing," *Review of Educational Research*, 38(1), February, 1968.

Glennon, V. J. "Testing Meaning in Arithmetic," *Arithmetic 49*, Supplementary Educational Monographs, No. 70. Chicago: University of Chicago Press, 1949, pp. 64-74.

Gray, Roland F. "An Approach to Evaluating Arithmetic Understandings," *The Arithmetic Teacher*, XIII, March, 1966, 187-191.

Greene, C. E., and G. T. Buswell. "Testing, Diagnosis, and Remedial Work in Arithmetic," Report of the Committee on Arithmetic, *Twenty-Ninth Yearbook*, National Society for the Study of Education, Part I, Chapter 5. Bloomington, Ill.: Public School Publishing Co., 1930.

Hoffman, B. *The Tyranny of Testing*. New York: Collier Books.

Lehew, C. "The Performance of Four- and Five-Year-Old Children in Operation Head Start on Selected Arithmetic Abilities," *The Arithmetic Teacher*, 15:1, 1968, 53-59.

Myers, S. S. *Mathematics Tests Available in the United States*. Washington, D.C.: National Council of Teachers of Mathematics, April, 1959. (New edition in press.)

National Council of Teachers of Mathematics. "The Evaluation of Learning in Arithmetic," *Sixteenth Yearbook*. Washington, D.C.: The Council, 1941.

Peak, P. et al. "Aids for Evaluators of Mathematics Textbooks," *The Arithmetic Teacher*, May, 1965, 388-394.

Sato, R. "Commentary on the International Study of Achievement in Mathematics," *The Arithmetic Teacher*, 15:2, 1968, 103-107.

Saunders, Norris. *Classroom Questions: What Kinds?* New York: Harper & Row, 1966.

Steffe, L. P. "The Relationship of Conservation of Numerousness to Problem-Solving Abilities of First-Grade Children," *The Arithmetic Teacher*, 15:1, 1968, 47-52.

Stroud, James B. *Psychology in Education*. New York: David McKay Co., 1946, p. 476.

Sueltz, B. A., et al. "The Measurement of Understanding in Elementary School Mathematics," *The Measurement of Understanding*. Forty-fifth Yearbook, Part I, National Society for the Study of Education, 1946, 138-156.

Tyler, Ralph W. "A Generalized Technique for Constructing Achievement Tests," *Educational Research Bulletin*. Columbus, Ohio: Ohio State University Press, X, 1931.

Weaver, J. F. "Big Dividends from Little Interviews," *The Arithmetic Teacher*, II, April, 1955, 40-47.

Index